MODEL ENGINEERING GUIDE

Simple
WORKSHOP
PROJECTS

PSL MODEL ENGINEERING GUIDE

Simple
WORKSHOP
PROJECTS

STAN BRAY

PATRICK STEPHENS

First published in 1988

British Library Cataloguing in Publication Data

Bray, Stan
  Simple workshop projects. — (PSL model engineering guide; 4).
  1. Engineering models
  I. Title
  620'.00228   TA177

  ISBN 0-85059-888-5

Patrick Stephens Limited is part of the Thorsons Publishing Group, Wellingborough, Northamptonshire, NN8 2RQ, England

Printed and Bound in Great Britain by Woolnough Bookbinding Limited, Irthlingborough, Northamptonshire

10 9 8 7 6 5 4 3 2 1

CONTENTS

INTRODUCTION

STARTING OUT

Writing a book of projects for the budding model engineer poses problems. It is a hobby which people start at vastly different levels, some are fortunate enough to be able to go out and purchase what is virtually a complete workshop, others just a second-hand lathe of uncertain vintage. Many start with one of the small lathes that are now available; excellent machines with the advantage that they can be put away in a drawer or cupboard when the day's modelling is finished. Then there is the question of skills. Some who enter the hobby are already highly skilled engineers, frequently having retired and wishing to continue their love of engineering. Some have just touched on engineering during craft studies at schools, while others have never done anything like it before in their lives.

The projects then must be designed to help people at all levels, and I hope these are. It is, of course, very tempting to start by building the traction engine or locomotive which has so long been the apple of your eye, but attempting this with no previous experience can mean disaster. When a person starts out in life and decides that engineering is his or her vocation, then either a college or university training, or perhaps an apprenticeship, is the first step they take. Therefore it is not really reasonable to assume that we can just step straight in to model engineering without some form of learning process.

Recalling my early days on the shop floor, training consisted at times of the most boring of exercises; filing a 1in cube from a piece of 1¼in round bar, for example, and having to eventually get it perfect. Good training, but hardly the sort of thing that those taking up engineering as a hobby want to do. What I have done in this book therefore is to think out a series of relatively simple projects that develop these skills, and yet in the end those who successfully complete them will have something which will be of use to them as model engineers.

Of the various tools to be constructed, some cannot be purchased anyway. Those like the graduating or slotting tool and the radiusing device can only be made in the home workshop and yet they are invaluable. Although machine vices and knurling tools can be bought, not so the knurling tool in the form described here, which is particularly useful for the model engineer. The dividing attachment for the lathe is something you will wonder how you ever did without.

MATERIALS AND METHODS

All of these items are simply made from pieces of metal cut to size and screwed together, and no welding or brazing is involved. Making them will enable you to teach yourself to saw and file accurately, and to drill and tap correctly, skills not quite as easy to acquire as they sound.

I have advocated the use of modern materials and in particular the use of cyanoacrylic adhesive. Until this became available a few years ago, there was a great deal more involved in lining up parts accurately than there is now; it certainly makes life a lot easier for the beginner. The use of retaining compounds also means that there is no longer any need for the press fitting together of components. In the descriptions of the projects which follow you will find frequent reference to securing items with a retainer. This just means applying a drop of suitable retaining compound and letting that do the work for you. I would suggest that the reader gets a leaflet from one of the manufacturers of these products so that he or she knows what is the correct material to use for the situation. Loctite, or Permabond, both available in a number of different strengths for various purposes, are probably two of the most popular with model engineers (see Appendix).

Most of the projects employ methods that are not generally standard engineering practice. For instance, sliding components are made by a process of building up, with two or more pieces of metal, whereas in most engineering workshops, dovetailed slides would have been used instead. This is quite deliberate. The machining of dovetails and the milling of tee slots is heavy work requiring very rigid equipment and, for the beginner to the hobby, is probably better left alone. The methods described will work quite well even though they are not standard practice.

Some of the metal specified for the tools is quite substantial, in particular that used for the vertical slide. As a rule, such material is often not available through normal model engineering suppliers, although it is often worth checking to see just what they can supply, as some now do keep very heavy sections of metal and will cut it to the right size for you. Personally I have found that if a visit is made to a local engineering factory, then usually what is required can be obtained from their scrap box for very little cash. It is always worth acquiring hefty chunks of metal if available and putting them by for possible use in the future, as throughout our model engineering we are constantly going to need such items. If they cannot be bought as scrap, then a look at the yellow pages will usually give you details of a steel stockist. Here too there is frequently a scrap box that can be raided cheaply, and if not, if the metal is a heavy section, then more often than not a cutting service is available enabling you to buy only what you require.

A word of warning at this point, however. Do not expect a piece of cut metal to be square. It is a most unlikely event and happens about as frequently as a total eclipse of the moon! The metal will have to be made square and this is where the acquiring of skills comes in. Do not go out and buy a length of metal specially, just because you do not fancy sawing a piece to size. The correct use of a hacksaw is a skill—almost an art – that must be acquired, and the sooner the better. If not, then valuable work will later be destroyed when a piece virtually finished needs to be sawn and is spoilt in the process. The sawing of metal is good for developing skills, and probably for the soul too.

The thought of having to saw through a piece of say 3in (75mm) square mild steel bar is at first pretty daunting. If, however, a good coarse blade is used and no attempt is made to hurry the strokes it is not so bad as it sounds. I usually do it in stages; cutting for a few minutes at a time and then working on something else for a while before returning to the sawing again.

SIZES AND MEASUREMENTS

There are hardly any measurements given in the book. Suggestions for sizes, yes, but measurements definitely not. This may seem strange to some, and may in some ways even make life difficult for those who are unsure how to start. Measurements would not, however, be practical. If the book was entitled *Projects for the Myford Lathe* or *Projects for the Unimat,* then measurements would be feasible. However, bearing in mind that the readers of this book will probably have between them many different types of lathe all requiring different sizes of equipment, it will soon be seen why quoting specific measurements is not practical. The reader must therefore work on proportions. Use the drawings by taking a size to suit your own lathe. Make all the other parts in direct proportion to it and the projects will work out correctly. No machines other than a lathe and a simple drilling machine (even a hand-drill on a stand will do) are required, so they should all be within the capabilities of every handyman.

Only the steam engines are dimensioned. This is quite deliberate, and is explained in the text. On those drawings that do have dimensions, both metric and imperial measurements are given. This is because at the time of writing both forms of measurements are in use. On the drawings the imperial measurements are shown in fraction form and have the standard abbreviation " to indicate inches. The metric measurements are given in millimetres ('mm') in some cases. However, in some instances it is just not physically possible to find space for the whole of the metric form to be printed, in which case a figure only is given. Since such a situation relates to millimetres only the metric figures can be easily distinguished from the imperial ones.

THE DRAWINGS

I have already indicated how the form of construction for all these projects has been considerably simplified. The text contains fairly comprehensive constructional details and if these are followed with reference to both photographs and drawings, construction should be relatively simple.

The drawings have been made as simple as possible and have been kept in a single form, what are called orthographic projections, as well as deliberately simplified to help those with only limited knowledge. For instance, an outline of the subject is shown in line form only. Where possible, and if doing so will be of any practical value, drawings of the subject are also shown from a different view. There may therefore be a front view, side view and top view. Some of the projects really have no front or side and so just two or three views may be given without any comment.

Where there are points that are hidden from view, the outline of these is shown in the form of a dotted line. If there are so many such items that it would make the drawing needlessly complicated, only the more important ones are shown in this form. This applies in particular to bolts, a profusion of which can make a drawing almost beyond comprehension!

Screw threads are shown as double lines and, where hidden, as double dotted lines. Again we have a situation where the showing of double dotted lines in some cases would cause complication and so it is possible that just the single dotted outline will be shown. However, careful study of both photographs and drawings will reveal what is required.

Again, if it is thought that such drawings will assist construction, various parts have been drawn separately showing details that may not be practically shown on the main drawings. These too may be shown from different positions.

FINISHING

I have not given a great deal of explanation on finish. Basically, a good rubbing along the grain of the metal with fine emery paper is recommended. I have described engine turning which gives a pleasant result. There are no chemical colouring methods shown, but I have painted some of the larger items that I have made. There is always the possibility that a large amount of very bright metal in a workshop will suffer from discolouring by either rust or general dulling over a period of time. Painting will help to prevent this, so less maintenance will be involved. How the projects are finished is, of course, a matter for the constructor and I can only say what I myself have done.

LOOKING AHEAD

Although a skilled worker could make many of the preliminary projects in a very short space of time, the less experienced are advised to take their time in the construction. It is all too easy to rush things and then make mistakes when a little careful thought would have prevented such errors and the associated disappointment.

Looking ahead to the second part of the book, this could be described as simple steam. An oscillating engine may not sound a very exciting prospect, but in point of fact it is the easiest way of learning how a steam engine works. Personally, I find them absolutely fascinating to build and again they can be made from odds and ends of scrap material, so that knowledge can be gained at very little cost. If a pair of cylinders for a large-scale locomotive is ruined in manufacture, we are talking about the loss of a great deal of time and money. The simple oscillating engine can be ruined a dozen times for virtually no cost at all. Of course, I hope they will not be ruined, but the making of them will teach the reader many things about steam engine construction.

Finally, all the projects are there as a guide. Most model engineers often like to put their own ideas into practice, and this is only to be applauded. I hope, then, that many of those reading this book will take my ideas and convert them to make something particular to themselves. This is how our hobby progresses, and if I have sown the seeds of innovation I shall be delighted.

1 *A MACHINE VICE*

The method used in constructing the machine vice, where a sliding component is required, is virtually the same as for making the other tools described in this book. A screw is used to drive the moving jaw, and the vice is built up from stock materials, the parts being systematically screwed together whilst held in position with cyanoacrylic adhesive (Figure 1). Each time I use this method I have to think back on how much time it saves when compared with the older ideas of clamping parts together, soldering them or fixing with dowels.

As with all the other tools, the vice can be made to any size the reader requires and, in fact, over the years I have made them in

The completed machine vice.

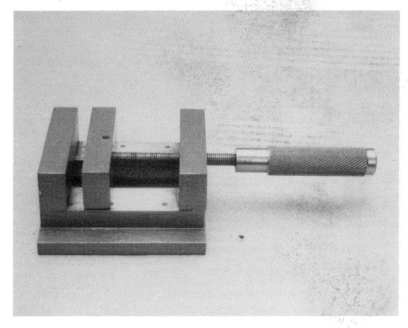

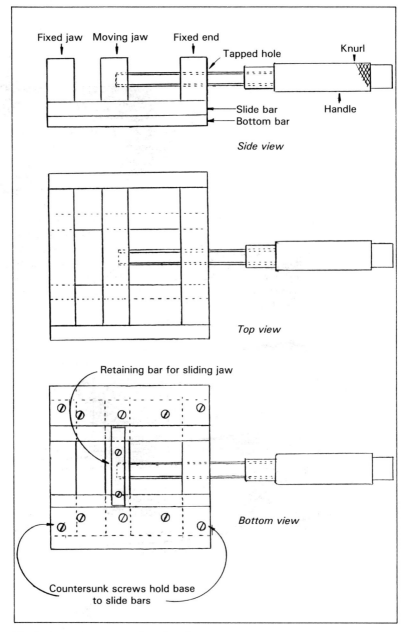

Fig 1 *General construction details.*

many different sizes. I would suggest that any increase or decrease in size is done proportionally in order to ensure that the vice remains functional. Having said that, however, one reason for making such a vice might be for use in a particular job where an unusual size of metal has to be held. In such cases, the variations can be made as desired or as necessary. For example, the opening can be made greater, or the jaws twice or even three times as long if that will suit the particular work. For normal everyday use, however, the vice shown is just about right.

We start with three pieces of mild steel for the opening jaw and the two ends. I used bright mild steel, but there is no reason why black should not be used if some spare pieces happen to be about the workshop. The pieces I used were ¾ x ½in and about 2½in long (18 x 12 x 60mm). The length of each piece will need to be identical and the ends should be square. The best way to achieve this is to stick all three together and, when set, put them in the four-jaw chuck and face the end square. Repeat for the other end and then all three pieces must be right. Make sure, though, that the top edges are flush with each other when they are stuck together, or you will find that the ends will not finish up square. When they have been machined, separate them with a smart tap from a plastic mallet and clean off the glue residue with a scraper.

We now need to make the slide bars to which the ends are to be secured and along which the moving jaw will run. Two pieces are required each 1 x ⅜in and about 3in long (25 x 10 x 75mm). Once again, either bright or black steel will do. Machine the ends square as described in the previous paragraph, and then scribe a line across each end. If using the measurements given above, the line will be ¼in (6mm) from the end; if using other sizes, the line should be half the width of the bar from the end. These are to act as a guide for drilling the holes for the screws that will secure the parts together. We are not going to centre punch on the line, however, but diagonally about ⅛in (3mm) either side of it, which will help to give extra strength (see diagram). At this stage we need only two holes — later a third will be added to form a triangle, the only figure that cannot be pushed out of shape without altering the length of one of the sides. In other words if we were to drill two or three holes in a straight line, the ends of the vice could twist, but by arranging the screws in the form of a triangle they cannot move. When marked out and centre punched, drill the holes in the tapping size for the screw you will use. I would suggest 5BA or 3mm. De-burr the backs of the holes where the drill breaks through with a countersink or a larger drill bit.

Use a square as a guide and, using your cyanoacrylic adhesive, stick both ends across both of the slide bars, as we will now call them. Make absolutely sure they are square, and be careful not to stick the square to the work. Leave to set, then drill all eight holes right through the end pieces with the same sized drill. Open out and countersink the holes in the slide bars, and tap a thread in those in the ends. I did not then separate the parts to do this but left them glued together. I am quite convinced that for light work the glue alone would suffice, but being a coward I preferred to do a 'belt and braces' job. Finally screw the parts together (Figure 2).

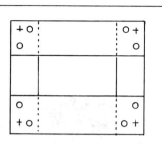

Fig 2 *Slide bar construction.*

Sketch shows initial hole positions; the crosses show final holes to be drilled through base.

The bottom bars come next and these were 1 x ³⁄₁₆in (25 x 5mm) and the same length as the upper ones. Mark out and drill, using the same sized drill as before, once again being sure to de-burr the holes. The bottom bars need to be offset out by about ³⁄₁₆in (5mm). So, when glueing them to the slide bars, lay a piece of suitably sized steel along the edge to ensure that the spacing is even. Drill through into the slide bars, and then, as before, open out and countersink the bottom bar, tap the slide bars and screw together.

We now need four holes, one at each end, which should be marked out and centre punched, being careful to make sure that the holes miss the existing screws securing the end pieces and also, as explained above, form a triangle for strength (see diagram). Again open out, countersink and tap. Use screws long enough to go through the bottom plate and slide bar and well into the ends.

The final job is to fill all the screw holes where the drill has gone right through. There should be six in each end plate, and three in each runner. Get some iron filings, mix up some epoxy adhesive such as Araldite and mix the iron filings with it. Fill the holes, then place the job on a gentle heat overnight (I put mine on the radiator). When the adhesive is set hard, clean it off level with a file and emery paper, and the holes will hardly show at all.

Fig 3 *Moving jaw.*

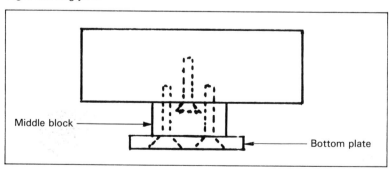

Middle block

Bottom plate

The assembled parts of the moving jaw.

The moving jaw can be dealt with next (Figure 3). Lay the vice upside down and put the jaw in position ensuring that it lines up with the end plates. Stick the middle block to it, after it has been drilled, then drill through when the glue is set and finish as before. Make sure that none of the glue spills over or the jaw will not move.

Drill the small bottom plate with two holes, that will go on either side of the screw in the middle block. Remove the jaw from the vice and stick the bottom plate in position. Drill and tap as before. The bottom plate will, of course, have to be removed before the vice can be assembled. When it is assembled, check for tight spots, and if there are any just ease them out with a file.

The handle is a piece of round bright mild steel, more or less of a size to suit your hand. Knurling it is optional; I think it helps but

Fig 4 *Adjusting screw.*

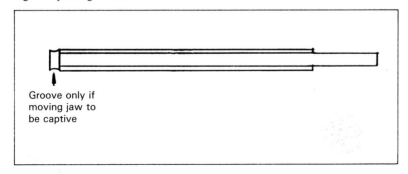

Groove only if
moving jaw to
be captive

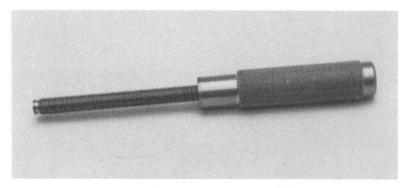

The handle and adjusting screw of the machine vice. The recess at the end of the screw is used to keep it in contact with the jaw, if one wishes. It is concave, and a grub screw through the moving jaw locating in the groove, prevents the lead screw coming away from the jaw.

others may not agree. Another idea is to use hexagonal material. The screw (Figure 4) is a piece of commercial studding with a ¼in (6mm) thread. Drill and tap the handle to accept the studding and then turn the locating groove in the end before sticking it into the handle with retaining compound.

One end piece (the fixed end) now has to be marked out and drilled to tapping size to take the thread on the handle. When this has been done, clamp the moving jaw to that end and drill through about half way. Take out the moving jaw again and open the hole out to clearance size for the thread, then cross drill and tap to take a grub screw. The fixed end of the vice should then also be tapped to take the handle.

Left *Drilling through the fixed end on the machine vice for the screw that will operate the movable jaw.*

Right *Using the drilled hole in the fixed end to locate the hole for the lead screw which moves the jaw. If one so wishes, there is no need to make this more than a dimple mark, since there is nothing at all wrong in the jaw being left loose. The vice shown completed has, in fact, its adjusting screw located in a recess and the thread held in position with an allen headed grub screw.*

To secure the moving jaw to the thread a small ball bearing is dropped down the hole and then the grub screw tightened up just sufficiently to engage the groove in the end of the studding on the handle and prevent the thread pulling out of the moving jaw when the vice is unscrewed. I finished the vice off with a hammered effect paint which I happened to have left over from another job. It gives it a good finish, but the vice could just as easily be cleaned up with emery and left bright, or painted with ordinary paint.

The underside of the machine vice showing the method of construction and the position of the screws.

That is all there is to it; a useful tool made from scrap material. It will probably take you longer to read the instructions than it will to make it! Its potential is obvious, and if suitable odds and ends of metal are saved up over the years then vices of various sizes can be made up as needed which will mean that after a few years there will be a vice available for every job. I counted up and found I have twelve machine vices of one sort or another and no matter what size the work piece is, I always have one suitable for holding it when I want to work on it.

2 *A TAILSTOCK DIE HOLDER*

Threading of components is not always as easy as it at first appears. Dies can cut threads at an angle which will render the finished item quite useless. It is therefore essential that care is taken to position the die correctly. Fortunately, when threading components on the lathe we have mechanical means to help us. One obvious situation that immediately springs to mind is the use of an ordinary hand type of die holder to thread a component held in the chuck. By setting the tool post square to the chuck, we can allow the die holder to rest against it and as the die progresses along the work, we can wind the cross slide along keeping the pressure on the die. The result should be a nice square thread. That sounds fine, so why make a special die holder?

When the die moves along the work it sometimes becomes impossible to keep the tool post in contact, particularly if the thread is to be longer than the width of the die. The thread will protrude through the die and foul the tool post, and even though the thread has been started nice and straight, it can and will still

A simple tailstock die holder. Note the slot in the holder which locates in a pin, thus allowing the die to travel forward as the thread is cut, whilst preventing it from twisting round.

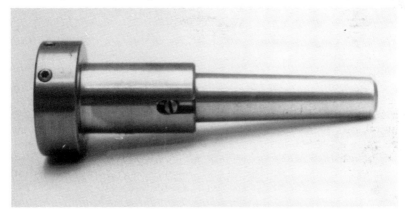

The larger tailstock die holder in position. It slides along the morse taper arbor seen here in the tailstock of a lathe.

wander out of line. For this reason, a die holder held firmly in the tailstock is the best aid we can have. Having said that, and even though I hope readers will make such a tool, before we start let us first think a little about the threads we are going to make.

When turning a die straight on to a piece of bar, tremendous forces are set up as the cutting edges of the die are comparatively large. If we take for example a standard ¼in Whitworth thread, the outside diameter is 0.25in and the core is 0.2187in. This means that the cutting edge of the die has to take a total of nearly 0.032in (0.82mm) off the metal; rather a large amount even when taken with a normal cutting tool in a lathe. As threads become larger so the cut gets greater. Add to this the fact that the cutting action is rotating over a fairly large area and it can be seen what I mean by the forces involved. We therefore should never try to thread material with dies unless first of all screw cutting the thread on the lathe for at least two-thirds of its depth. Whilst this fact cannot easily be applied to very small fine threads, certainly anything of ¼in (5mm) or over should be dealt with in this way. Even so a considerable amount of force is still going to be needed to make a thread of say ½in (12mm) even if it has been partly pre-cut.

Having explained how great the forces are that are involved in the cutting of threads, the reasons for the variations I am going to suggest in making tailstock tool holders will, I hope, become obvious. Let us start anyway with the means of holding the die holder in the lathe. There are two ways of doing this: either by using it with a shank that will fit into the morse taper or by giving it one which will fit into the tailstock chuck. The latter is not really a very good idea although, for those who do not have facilities to turn a taper, it may be the only way. The difficulty comes in obtaining sufficient grip and stability with the tailstock chuck. Of necessity, the shank of the holder has to be of a fairly small diameter, and when put under pressure this can have a tendency to twist in the chuck. This is not often a problem providing the lathe is turned by hand but if power is used then we might start getting into difficulties. Therefore all the holders I am about to describe will have morse tapers. If you are not able to turn such a taper, then they can be purchased ready turned at quite reasonable prices. Failing the purchase of one, and after all one of the purposes of this book is to encourage people to make things, where I describe the taper, turn instead a step to fit the tailstock chuck. The rest of the tool is identical in every way.

To make the arbor on which the die holder is to fit, the top slide

Setting up the top slide for making a morse taper.

must be set over to the angle required for the morse taper in your tailstock. Start by putting a piece of bar in the chuck, and make a nice deep centre in it. Now take a normal tailstock centre and support it between another centre in the tailstock, and the hole in the bar which you have just made. Wind the tailstock up so that the centre which is supported at either end is held firmly in position. Next place a bar of metal in the tool post running parallel with the bed, and then turn the top slide round so that the metal bar lies flush with the morse taper of the supported centre. Take the bar from the tool post and replace it with a clock gauge. Wind the top slide backwards and forwards and see if there is any variation on the clock as the plunger runs along the morse taper. If there is, make minute adjustments to the top slide angle until the clock shows no variations at all. It takes longer to describe the operation than to do it, so don't be frightened of it.

Once the correct setting has been obtained, the taper can be turned on the bar of metal that is to be used as the tailstock fixing of the die holder. Start at the small end and work towards the chuck. Use only the cross slide and top slide, and make sure that the apron is well and truly locked so that it doesn't move during operations. Check the small diameter and when it is reached you have your morse taper. You will see from the drawings that there is a parallel section at the thicker end (Figure 5). For larger lathes this can be stepped down, but on smaller varieties it may have to remain at the same diameter as the large end of the taper. Some of these small lathes, by the way, have short tapers, or half tapers. If that is so, make yours the same; there is little point in trying to make a full taper as the lathe tailstock will not accept it.

The diagrams show three types of die holder bodies. One (Figure 6) fits into a pin in the tailstock adapter and is useful for threading under power. The die will run along the workpiece and when the

Fig 5 *Morse taper section.*

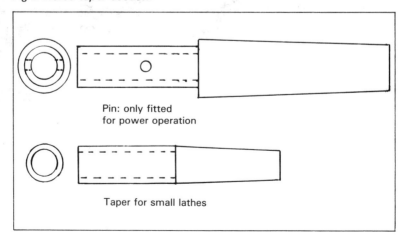

Pin: only fitted
for power operation

Taper for small lathes

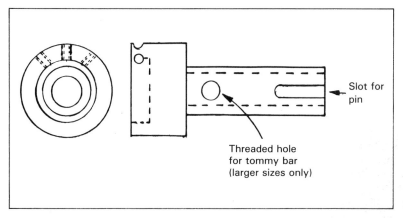

Fig 6 *Body.*

slot reaches the end of the pin the holder will rotate. The pin should go right through the parallel section of the taper bar in order to give it sufficient support. The tailstock can then be wound in a little if a longer thread is required. The die holder itself is a bar of metal bored out to fit over the tailstock fitting and then bored out more to take the die.

There are several different sizes of die and the following table gives the British sizes.

British die sizes

Outside diameter		Thickness	
(in)	(mm)	(in)	(mm)
$^{13}/_{16}$	17.5	$^{1}/_{4}$	6
1	25.4	$^{5}/_{16}$	8
$1^{5}/_{16}$	31.5	$^{3}/_{8}$	10
$1^{1}/_{2}$	37.5	$^{1}/_{2}$	12

There are also some metric dies available, although at the time of writing, as far as I can establish, all British-made dies, whether for imperial or metric threads, are of the old British imperial sizes. Continental ones have their own sizes and some American ones also differ.

It will be seen from the diagram that the holder is turned to a step where it fits on to the arbor, making it more convenient to handle. The step can, if desired, be turned before boring if that makes for easier working. The slot can be milled out if facilities are available, or it can be sawn and filed to shape and size. It is a good idea to make two or three holders for whatever dies you have available. For the larger sizes, where they will be used for heavy threading, a hole should be drilled and tapped to take a tommy bar

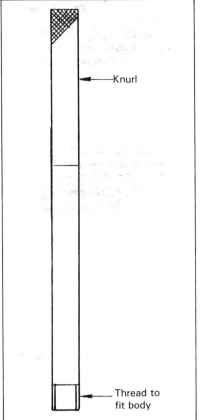

Above *Four different sizes of die holders, all of which fit on the same morse taper arbor.*

←—Knurl

Left Fig 7 *Tommy bar.*

Below Fig 8 *Double-ended body.*

←— Thread to fit body

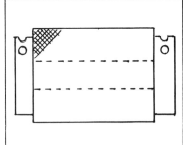

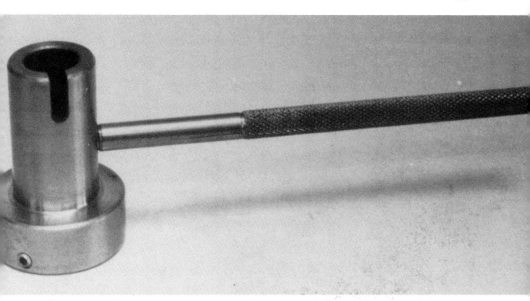

The die holding section of the tailstock die holder. The slot and tommy bar can be clearly seen.

in order to prevent the die holder turning when under pressure (Figure 7). For smaller-sized dies, the fixture in the morse taper will be sufficient and a tommy bar is not necessary. However, there would be nothing wrong with fitting a tommy bar even to the smaller holder if it was felt that it would assist operations.

The second type of die holder is double-ended (Figure 8). It has one size of recess at one end and a different size at the other. The length of the holder is knurled to give a grip; there is no means by which this type of die holder can be fitted over the pins described for the previous type, and it must be gripped by the hand to prevent it from turning when in use. A tommy bar could be fitted, but this would probably mean making the holder very much longer in order to get a sufficient length on the tailstock end. This type has some advantage in that it is convenient to have just the one holder for two sizes, and, provided that when the larger end is in

A double ended die holder. It is not practical to fit a retaining slot and so when in use the holder must be held by the hand. This is the reason for the extra-long knurling.

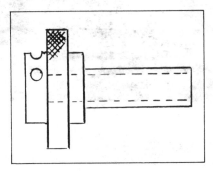

Above *This smaller tailstock die holder is designed for use on the very small lathes. The outer diameter is raised in comparison and this is used to grip the holder; the slot idea, as described for the larger lathes, would prove unsuitable in the circumstances.*

Left Fig 9 *Body for small lathe.*

use the threads have been partly pre-cut, it should create no problems.

The third holder is designed for the smaller lathe (Figure 9). Again, there is no retaining pin since it is not very practical at this size. It is also unlikely that large threads are going to be cut on the smaller lathe and so there is also no tommy bar. What has been done, though, is to increase slightly the outside diameter of the holder and knurl it to provide a better grip.

The question I have so far avoided is the drilling of the three holes that take the retaining screws that hold the dies in place. Here again there are differences in positioning, but fortunately most conform to a set pattern. The holes are usually at 45° to each other but the angle is taken from the inside of the recess for the die which makes things a little difficult. To help me I drill a tiny hole through where the centre screw is to go. I then set a pair of dividers to the correct distance on the die and I use these to mark the inside edge of the die recess. Next I place the holder in the three jaw chuck and bring the mark to just touch the tip of an ordinary turning tool, held at the correct height in the tool post. I

The tailstock die holder for the smaller lathe in position in the tailstock.

slide the tool along the face of the die holder, using the cross slide handle, and then along the outside edge of the holder. I now have a scribed mark exactly in line with the inside of the die holder where the screw is to be drilled. It is then just a case of getting it the correct distance from the edge of the holder, after which it can be centre punched, drilled through square and tapped to whatever size you intend to use. The operation can be repeated for the third screw.

The type of screw used is a matter of personal choice. If you wish, you can use those with a protruding head, but personally I use either the allen type grub screw or a slotted grub screw.

A tap holder is described in the next project and this makes use of the same morse taper arbor as the die holder, thus saving some work. It follows, though, that the morse taper section must have a suitable hole through the centre to take the shank of the tap holder. This will also allow for the cutting of long threads when used with a die holder.

3 *A TAP HOLDER*

The tapping of screw threads can be a difficult operation. Taps often appear to have a mind entirely of their own and if they decide not to go into the hole straight, then it is very difficult to persuade them otherwise. Whilst, therefore, the tap wrench has a definite part to play in workshop operations, for good accurate work we need some means of ensuring that taps enter the work properly. At the same time, because they have a nasty habit of breaking off inside the hole, we also need to be able to carry out the tapping operation as gently as possible.

Work that is held in the lathe should always be tapped with the tailstock acting as a guide. Thus, the obvious answer is to put the tap in the tailstock chuck and rotate the mandrel where the work is held. This is fine for a very large diameter tap, and in fact the lathe can probably even be allowed to work under its own power whilst the operation is carried out. However, when we use small taps, it is a different matter entirely and some sort of device is needed for securing the tap whilst still allowing it to be used gently. There are several ways in which this can be done and there is no reason why a separate device, a tapping machine, should not be made up just for carrying out tapping operations. Personally though, I find the workshop is always so full of machinery that I cannot move around and so I am going to suggest that we make use of part of the tailstock die holder already described in the previous project.

The morse taper section of the arbor has a hole down through the centre, so if our tap holder is made to slide into that hole, the holder can slide forward as the tap works its way into the metal. If we were to use the tap fixed directly into the tailstock chuck, the whole lathe tailstock would of course be pulled along the lathe bed by the tap and you can imagine the strain this puts on both the tap and the workpiece.

A chuck is a convenient way of holding a tap and there is no reason why a tapping device should not be made with a small chuck on the end to grip the tap. However, I feel that whilst the system would work, even the smallest chuck is not suitable for very tiny taps. There is also the difficulty of the chuck having to

A tailstock tapholder seen here in position in the same morse taper arbor used for the die holder. This saves time when in use, as well as the effort of making two tapers when one will do both jobs.

grip the round part of the tap shank, and this means that it is often difficult to prevent the tap from rotating inside the chuck. There are flats on the end of tap shanks and these are there to provide a positive means of holding them, so they should in my opinion be used.

Unfortunately this will mean making several sizes of tap holder, a separate one being required for each size of shank. Luckily the manufacturers are rather kind to us here and as a rule they make several sizes of tap with the same-size shank. This means, of course, that whilst we still need several sizes of holder, we do not need to have one for every tap. Fortunately, making a holder is only a matter of a few minutes' work and is no great hardship. They can be made from odd scraps of material and whether they are made identically or not is a matter for the individual. My own collection is something like 'Topsy' — it just growed. Possibly, if I was making a fresh start, I would cut up a suitably sized piece of

Left *A small tailstock tap holder for use on smaller lathes. The shank is shorter and the holder has been built up rather than turned to shape. The collar is held in position with retaining compound.*

Left *A knurled collar made for fixing over the shaft of a small tap holder. This form of construction saves material and makes a neat job.*

Below *The small tailstock holder fitted into a short morse taper which is typical of those used on the smaller lathes.*

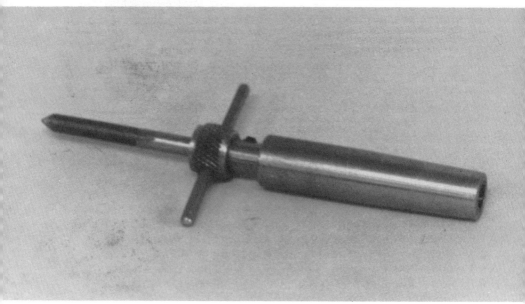

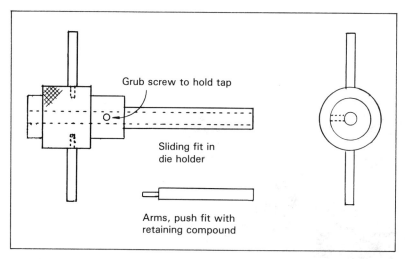

Fig 10 *General construction details.*

metal bar and make all the holders identical, for no other reason than that they will look better. Who knows — one day I may even get round to replacing the old ones and end with a matching set.

The actual manufacture of the head will need little description. A suitable length of bar — I would suggest about 1½ to 2in (37 to 50mm) would be about right — is turned down for about two-thirds of its length to the diameter necessary to fit the inside of the tailstock. The metal is then reversed in the chuck, and the hole for the tap drilled after centring. The large diameter should be knurled. I always turn a short length of the metal either side of the knurling to a smaller diameter. It serves no useful purpose but looks better that way as can be seen from the illustration.

The work can now be taken from the lathe and the hole for the screw that will secure the tap can be cross drilled and tapped to take a suitable grub screw. For taps of ⅛in (3mm) or over I would suggest the holder is cross drilled again on opposite sides and arms inserted and held in place with retaining compound. This will give a little extra grip when using the tap. It is not wise to use such bars for smaller sizes, as too much pressure could be exerted and the tap broken too easily.

Should you decide that you prefer to use a chuck, instead of making the hole for the tap, drill and tap the holder with a thread suitable to take a small chuck of the type used on DIY drills. The cross drilling for the small tommy bars will still be needed so that the holder can be gripped when tapping.

That takes care of tapping operations in the lathe, but what about work that will not easily fit the lathe such as flat plate? The correct tool for this is known as a staking tool and is not so very different or difficult to make, but again we arrive at the situation of the workshop becoming more and more cluttered. Personally, I

The tailstock tapping attachment can be used to get threads square in plate as well. A hole is simply drilled into a suitably sized metal bar and the holder is held in that using the drilling machine chuck to keep it at a perfect ninety degree angle.

use the same tapping head but working in a metal bar gripped by the chuck on the drilling machine, this bar being drilled to take the tapping head. The tap can then be allowed to screw itself into the work whilst being rotated by the tommy bars, and it will go in perfectly straight, always provided, of course, that the drilling machine table is square with its chuck.

Do not forget when tapping that the use of some form of cutting lubricant is essential with all materials except plastic or cast iron. The commercial tapping compounds are ideal for most occasions and they are relatively cheap to buy. A good alternative is lard, which, if robbed from the household fridge, works out even cheaper. Liquid soap works well on aluminium as does white spirit. Do not forget that the tap must be withdrawn at frequent intervals to clear the swarf.

4 AN INDEXING ATTACHMENT

Dividing is not a luxury when practising model engineering — it is a necessity. There are hundreds of examples that could be given where the division of the surface of the workpiece is necessary. Making nuts is an obvious one, but there are many more occasions when division is required. Fortunately, assuming that your lathe is capable of screw-cutting operations, we have an easy means of division readily to hand in the change wheels that are used to create the chain of gears for screw cutting. If one of these gears not in use is attached to the lathe mandrel and held securely in a set position, then by using the teeth we have access to an almost infinite number of divisions. For example, suppose we use a gearwheel with forty teeth. If we can fix every tooth in the wheel at a set position, we can obtain forty divisions in one revolution. If we take every fourth tooth we will have ten divisions and by taking every tenth tooth, four divisions. There are usually quite a number of gearwheels available and the use of these will ensure that most divisions required can be obtained, as long as they are the same or less than the largest gearwheel.

An even easier way of obtaining three or four divisions is to cut a length of wood to size so that one end rests on the lathe bed and the other fits under one of the chuck jaws. If the jaws are rested on this and then rotated as required, we can have two, three or four divisions by using the three-jaw or four-jaw chucks. Personally I always use this method for these two particular divisions because I am too idle to fix my dividing attachment into position, when I can do things the easy way!

However, let us assume that readers of this book either want more divisions than that or are not as idle as I am, and let us see how to go about obtaining these divisions in the easiest possible way. To do this we must make use of the lathe's hollow mandrel. Like all the projects in this book, exact details of the whole device cannot be given as its manufacture and size will depend on the type and size of lathe in use, but whatever the lathe we will need a piece of mild steel rod to make the body which slides easily into the mandrel and is about half its length. The degree of fit should be

The indexing attachment in use. The plunger is secured in between two of the teeth of the gear used for the division. This is held in the lathe mandrel with the shaft and taper described.

such that there is no shake on the bar, whilst it should be able to slide easily into the hole.

A hole is drilled or bored through the centre of this bar to take a piece of studding and so should be a clearance hole to suit the size of studding to be used. The studding itself can be either home-made or a commercial product, but ideally it should be about one-quarter or one-third of the diameter of the bar. One end of the bar is then drilled or bored out for about one-quarter of its length, so that the thickness of the wall is no more than $\frac{1}{16}$in (1.5mm). Finally, a saw cut is made lengthways along the rod (or perhaps I should now say tube), the length of the cut being about half the length of the wide part of the bore in which it is made. Both edges of the metal should have a slight chamfer to prevent it binding too much later on when it is expanded (Figure 11).

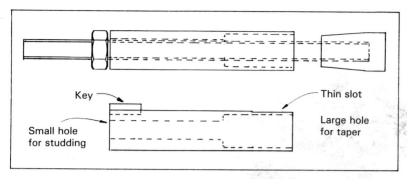

Fig 11 *Body.*

We now take a piece of the same material and drill and tap a hole in one end for the studding that is to be used. The same end is then tapered. To do this, the top slide will need to be set over. I set mine over by 2° which is about right for a lathe such as the Myford ML7. For a smaller lathe, half a degree less may be required. Again, the length of the taper will depend on the lathe, but I would suggest that it be about one-eighth of the length of the main bar. If the taper is made too shallow, by the way, it will be difficult to release. If made too steep, it will not grip. Fortunately, being so short, if you find it is not quite right, all is not lost as it can be put back in the chuck and the amount of taper adjusted slightly. Lastly, the tapered piece can be finished to its final length which is about one-and-a-half times that of the taper itself (Figure 12).

If we now return to the body, a slot must now be made at the end which has been bored with the small hole. This is to take a key

The mandrel assembly for the dividing attachment. The large diameters are a good but not tight fit in the hollow lathe mandrel. The taper fits into an enlarged hole in the longer part, and the studding is secured with retainer in the tapered piece and passes right through the parallel section. When tightened up, the parallel section expands because of a small slot that has been cut in the end.

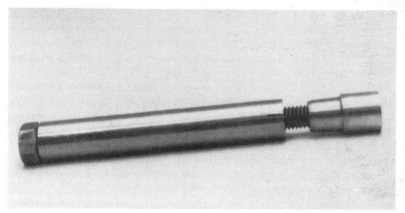

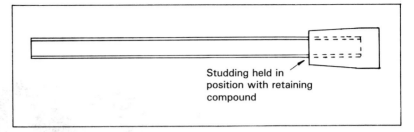

Studding held in
position with retaining
compound

Above Fig 12 *Taper section.*

Left *The gearwheel is retained on the shaft by means of a key. This involves making a small slot into which is inserted a piece of square steel. In this illustration the steel is held in position with cyanoacrylic adhesive.*

to hold the gear wheel in position. The size of the slot will have to be taken from the keyway in the gearwheel, and then a piece of steel can be held in the slot either by brazing or using a good cyanoacrylic adhesive.

A plunger (Figure 13) is the next item required, the end of which must be made to fit in between the teeth of the gearwheel which is being used. Usually a flat is filed on each side of the tooth on the plunger as shown in the drawing. This is the ideal but it may just be possible that some other shape will be required, depending upon the type of gearwheel in use on the particular lathe. The one shown will, I am quite sure, be suitable for the vast majority of lathes. Finally, I made a knob for the end of my plunger to make it easier to use. I simply bored a piece of mild steel rod of suitable

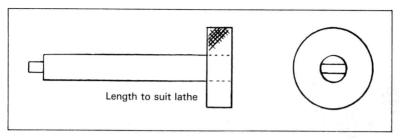

Above Fig 13 *Plunger.*

Below *The plunger used to locate the gearwheel at the correct position. The end section must be made to a good fit between the gearwheel teeth, in order to ensure accuracy.*

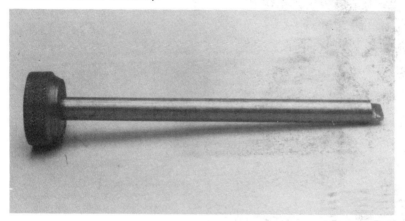

length and diameter and held it in position with retaining compound. When the compound had set I knurled it and just trimmed off the edges to make it look smart. This latter operation serves absolutely no useful purpose, and is purely cosmetic.

We now have the basic ingredients for the dividing attachment, and what is required now is a means of fitting it to the lathe. The part which fits into the mandrel and holds the gearwheel needs no more than a nut and possibly a washer, but the plunger requires some form of housing.

It is here that things will diversify very much according to the reader's lathe. Whatever make it may be, some form of attachment has to be made up to hold the plunger secure. The one shown in the illustration is made from a piece of steel plate about ⅛in (3mm) thick which simply bolts to the slot on the lathe where normally the cover for the gears is held. I chose this method as again laziness meant that I did not have to dismantle the change wheels each time I wanted to do some dividing. Other model engineers use the actual slots holding the change wheels which are usually on some form of bracket. This is probably more rigid than my method, but also more time-consuming when the device

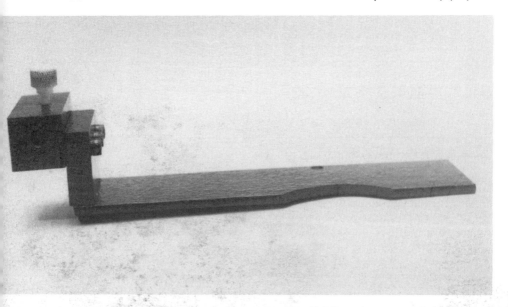

Above *The method of securing the dividing plunger must depend very much on the individual lathe to which it is to be fitted. The fitting here has been selected because of its simplicity, but some readers may, however, find that they have to make the fitting to bolt on to the change wheel supports rather than the guard support for which this fitting is intended.*

Right *The indexing attachment showing the method of fixing it to a Myford ML7 lathe. This idea will work with many types of lathe but some models do not have this type of cover fixing. In that case the reader will have to alter the bracket to make it fit a convenient point on the lathe in question.*

is in use. Whatever the answer, there must somewhere or other be a suitable place on your own particular lathe on which a bracket can be held to hold the plunger.

You will see that in my case the plunger itself is held in a piece of square mild steel bored to accommodate it. When located in the teeth of the gearwheel a set screw is tightened up to hold the plunger in position. The screw in the illustration was made from plastic rod but whatever material you use should be no harder than brass (it must be softer than the plunger itself to prevent the latter from becoming scored). The design of screw is up to the individual — it could be an ordinary commercial brass screw which is tightened up with a screwdriver if so desired, although personally I prefer one with a knurled head as I can never find a screwdriver at the vital moment!

An alternative to the screw is to put a collar on the plunger between the holder and the gearwheel and to fit a spring between the collar and the holder. This certainly saves a lot of bother in tightening the plunger, but it does limit the flexibility of the device.

This photograph was only possible as a result of the construction of three of the tools described in this book. The handle of the vertical slide (Project 8) is being graduated using the graduating tool (Project 5) to mark it and the indexing device constructed in this Project to make the necessary divisions.

If the spring is set to be used with a large gearwheel then it may not snap up onto a smaller one. Equally, if set for the small one it will not open wide enough for the large one. The set screw idea ensures that the plunger may be quickly adjusted to suit any size of wheel.

I think the method of using the device needs little or no description. A good tip though is to mark off on the gearwheels the divisions most likely to be used, thus saving the need to count the teeth each time. Usually, if you count them you will get half way through when the telephone rings and then you will have to start again! When the mandrel is released it may stick inside the lathe mandrel. If so, the taper can be freed by gently tapping the end of the studding. Should the main part stick, it will need some persuasion to release it from the chuck end of the lathe mandrel. A piece of steel rod with a short length of brass or copper on the end should be part of every model engineer's workshop equipment and will come in useful for tapping out morse tapers as well as this device.

5 *A GRADUATING AND SLOTTING TOOL*

When one first thinks about it, a graduating tool seems like a tool that is unlikely to be used very often and so one tends to question whether it is worth making. In fact, when it is made, it is surprising how often it can be brought into use. There are several examples given in this book where such a device will be very useful indeed. For many years it was something I kept putting off making on the grounds that it would rarely be used. During that time, whenever I made various items that would have been vastly improved by nice

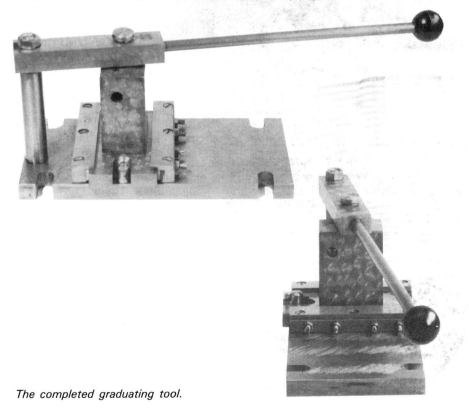

The completed graduating tool.

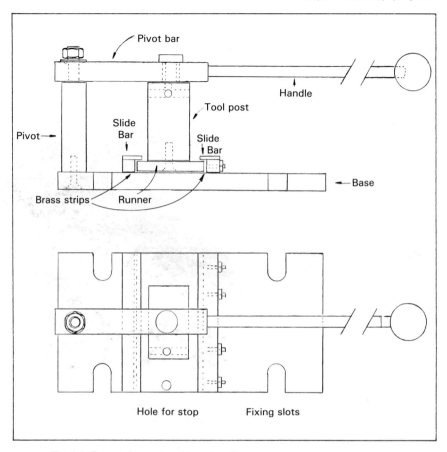

Fig 14 *General construction details.*

neat markings on collars and in other similar situations, I always
made these marks with a centre punch or a chisel, leaving a great
deal to be desired in both accuracy and appearance.

The graduating tool can also be used as a means of cutting small
slots in the workpiece either internally or externally. Of course,
external slots can be cut on a milling machine, and doing so, in
some ways, is easier, although this is not always the case. Often it
is desirable to cut a slot with the work still in position on the lathe.
The graduating tool will do that very simply. It is not designed for
cutting long slots but for short ones like keyways etc it will do very
well. If long slots were required, the tool would have to be made
with a screw traverse rather than the lever as described.

The size given can be modified to suit individual lathes. For the
smaller machines of up to 2in centre height, use material about
one-half to two-thirds of the sizes shown, although make sure that
the sizes selected are not too small otherwise the tool may then be
too weak.

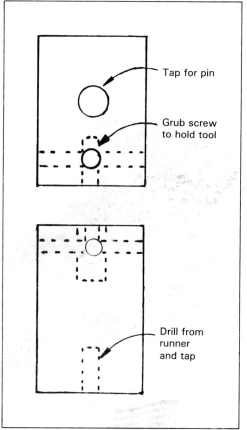

Tap for pin

Grub screw
to hold tool

Drill from
runner
and tap

Above *The tool post construction. The single hole is to hold
the cutting tool. The smaller of
the pair of tapped holes is to
take the securing screw for the
tool, and the larger is for the
pivot.*

Right Fig 15 *Tool post.*

The parts to start with when constructing the graduating tool
are the tool post (Figure 15) and the runner (Figure 16). For lathes
of about 3in centre height, the tool post should be made from a
piece of mild steel bar 1½in x 1in (37mm x 25mm). The length will
depend on the lathe, but it must be long enough when in place to
allow a cutting tool to be set at centre height. The runner is made
from a piece of ¼in (6mm) steel plate, 1½in x 2in (37mm x
50mm). Start by drilling the hole in the top of the tool post to suit
the pivot pin tapping size for whatever thread will be used. At the
same time, drill the hole which will take the screw that will
eventually secure the cutting tool, using a tapping size to suit the
grub screw to be used. Then cross drill the hole for the cutting tool
at lathe centre height and just a little way in from the end. You will
see from the illustration that a hole is also shown for a tool to be
held at the front of the post. I put this there in case it might prove
useful at some time. So far it has not been, but it is almost certain
that if I had not put it there, I would have had cause to use it!

Next, drill the two holes in the runner that will take the screws
that hold the tool post in position; drill them to tapping size, clean

Above *The runner with two countersunk holes for securing it to the tool post. The slot is for a stop if required.*

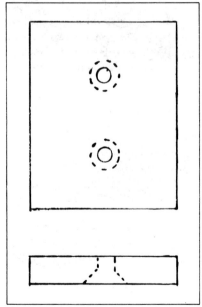

Left Fig 16 *Runner.*

off any burrs, and stick the tool post to the slide with a cyanoacrylic adhesive (I used Flex Zap in this case). When this has set, drill through the holes into the tool post to the required depth to suit the screws used. Providing the correct grade of adhesive has been used, there is no danger of the two parts separating while drilling. To part them simply, put the tool post in the vice and give the slide a smart tap with a copper mallet. When separated,

Fig 17 *Slide bars.*

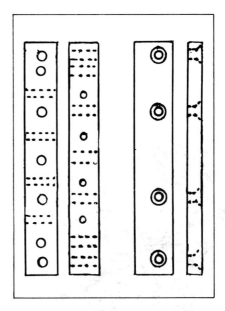

open out the two holes in the slide to clearance size and countersink them. Make sure the countersink is deep enough for the screw heads to be below the surface of the slide. A hole can then be drilled for the slot which takes the stop and this can be carefully sawn out with a sharp hacksaw. The stop is not an absolute necessity and so has not been shown on the drawings. If it is required then it should screw into a hole in the base. Finally, tap the holes at the bottom of the tool post, and the one for the grub screw, and remove all burrs.

The slide bars (Figure 17) are next and these are each made from two pieces of mild steel with a brass insert to take up wear. One piece of the steel is square and the other flat. The measurement of the square piece must be exactly the same as the thickness of the runner, so if the slide is ¼in (6mm) thick the steel bar must be ¼in (6mm) square. It could of course, be flat, say ¼ x ⅜in (6mm x 10mm) but the measurement of the two sides *must be identical* with the thickness of the runner. The flat material for the top part of the slides should be wider than the square bar but need only be ⅛in (3mm) in thickness. The brass should measure the same in width as the thickness of the slide and should be about ¹⁄₁₆in (2mm) in depth.

The slide bars are made directly in relation to the base. The base (Figure 18) is mild steel plate ⅜in (10mm) thick and 3in (75mm) wide with the length to suit the cross slide, although it can be slightly wider or thicker to suit the lathe requirement. Those making the tool for a small lathe should note that to maintain rigidity the thickness of the base must not be less than ¼in (6mm). Cover the base in marking fluid and, using a square, scribe a line across the width on the pivot end of the base where the screw

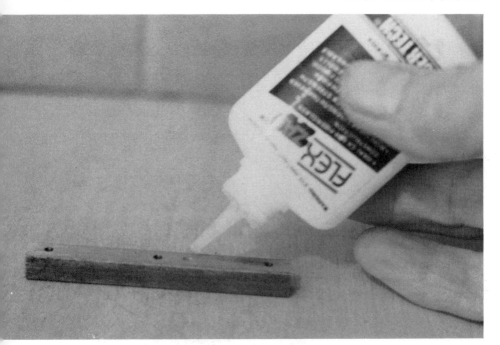

Above *After drilling one slide bar tapping size, adhesive is applied to allow the top to be held in position ready for drilling the second row of holes.*

Below Fig 18 *Base.*

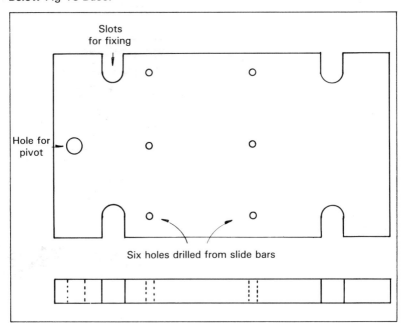

holes are to be marked. Leave enough material to allow for the pivot and for the slots for clamping the device to the cross slide. Drill the three securing holes through the square part of one of the slide bars to the tapping size for the thread to be used. With the cyanoacrylic adhesive, stick this to the base, using both the line and your square to fix it accurately. Take care not to stick the square to the work! When the adhesive is dry, using the holes in the slide bar as a guide, drill right through the base.

Drill the second square part of the slide bar in exactly the same way, and placing the two pieces of brass and the slide between the two square bars, glue the second one to the base. Do not forget that before sticking the parts together, all burrs should be removed. We should now have two square bars in position, with room for the slide to move between them with the two pieces of brass strip also in position.

Make sure you know which bar goes on which side and separate them from the base (you could mark them with a felt pen). Drill the two flat pieces for the tops, tapping size, and stick them to the bars, making sure they are carefully lined up. Drill through the two flat pieces and the square bars, using the tapping size drill, then drill the square bar that will be furthest away from the pivot pin with the four holes for the adjusting screws. Clamp a brass piece to this bar and drill recesses in it using the screw holes as a guide. These indentations will stop it sliding out of position in use. Stick the other brass strip to the other slide bar and drill through with two tapping sized holes. This piece will be captive on its slide bar.

There is now much opening out, tapping and countersinking to be done. The flat pieces are opened out clearance size and

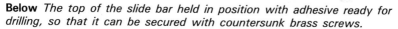

Below *The top of the slide bar held in position with adhesive ready for drilling, so that it can be secured with countersunk brass screws.*

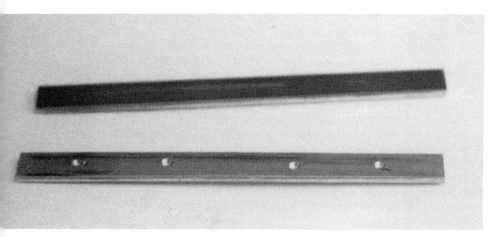

Above *The two brass strips. The nearest has recesses drilled in it into which fit the ends of the adjusting screws; it then acts as a gib strip.*

Below *One of the brass strips secured to the slide bar with brass screws, using the normal method of first securing with adhesive and then drilling through and tapping.*

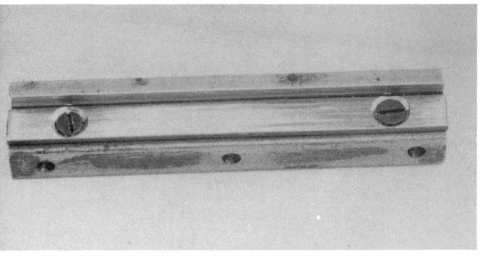

countersunk. The screw holes for the adjusters, and those for securing the second brass piece and the square slide bars are all tapped. The holes in the captive brass strip are opened out to clearance size and countersunk deep enough to make sure the screw heads are below the surface, when fully tight, likewise those in the flat strips that form the tops of the slide bars. You may as well at this stage open out and countersink the holes in the base, as well as marking out and drilling the holes for the pivot pillar and the stop (if used). The fixing slots should be drilled and cut to suit the T-bolt slots in your lathe, or if preferred, plain holes

Above *The adjustable side of the slide bars ready for screwing to the base.*

Below *The slide of the graduating tool (without the brass bearers at this stage). Notice the gib screws and nuts which later will allow adjustment of the action.*

can be used for securing the device to the lathe. Finally, tap the holes for the stop and the pivot pillar.

The pivot bar (Figure 19) is made from steel bar ¾ x ⅜in (18mm x 10mm). As usual, slightly thicker and/or wider will do just as well. Two holes are drilled in the wider surface, with the end one opened out to a slot as shown in the drawing. There is also a hole in the opposite end for the handle which is drilled lengthways and which should be done in the four-jaw chuck for the sake of accuracy. This hole can be tapped or it can be left plain and the handle held in with retainer.

Above *The brass gib strips are now in position. The left hand one is loose and can be adjusted while the right hand one is secured with countersunk brass screws. The hole drilled on the right of the base is for the pivot pin and the device at the end of the slide is a stop which can be added if desired (the stop position is not shown on the drawing as this will be a matter for the individual. It is not strictly necessary but can be useful when making graduations). The 'herringbone' finish has been obtained by scraping with a ground down file.*

Below Fig 19 *Pivot bar.*

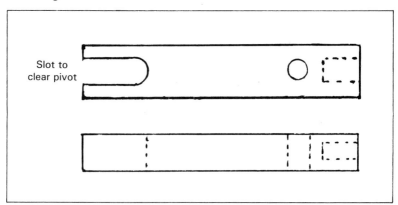

Slot to
clear pivot

A graduating and slotting tool 51

Right *The pivot bar. The hole is to take the pin for the tool post. The slot locates on the bronze, or brass, bush of the pivot.*

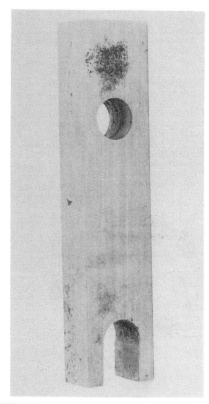

Below Fig 20 *Pivot and pivot pin (two types).*

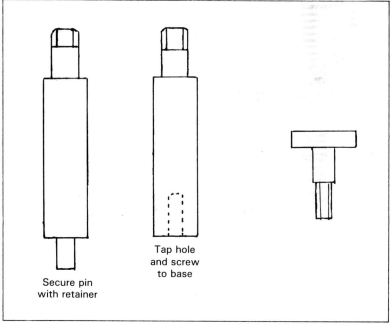

Secure pin
with retainer

Tap hole
and screw
to base

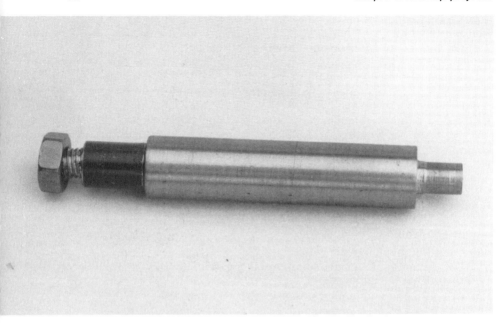

Above *The pivot pillar — note the bronze bush to prevent wear. The step turned at the opposite end can be threaded if one wishes, and a mating thread made in the base, or, as shown here, held in place with a retaining compound.*

Below *The pivot pin. Note the bush to prevent wear and the washer which allows an easy movement of the bar.*

Making the pivot pin is a straightforward turning and threading job, as is the pivot pillar (Figure 20). The boss on the pillar that fits into the base may be threaded, or the pillar can be held in with retainer. Obviously, if it is to be secured by this latter method then the hole in the base will not require tapping. I held mine with Permabond 168 (an anaerobic adhesive) and it has given no problems and did save the few minutes it would have taken to tap the base and thread the pillar. Two bronze bushes are required to prevent too much wear when the tool is used, and I have also placed a washer between the toolpost and the bush, again to save excessive wear.

The tool bit can be made of either high-speed steel or silver steel hardened and tempered (I actually used a broken end mill). The handle is a mild steel rod with either a plastic or steel ball on the end. The gib screws for adjusting the slide are short pieces of studding with screwdriver slots sawn in one end with ordinary nuts used for keeping the adjustment. The stop is a short piece of mild steel round bar threaded at one end, and screws into a similarly threaded hole in the base. This is then cross drilled and tapped and fitted with a screw to provide some adjustment. This stop helps to ensure that the graduations are the same length. For slotting, it can be removed if required.

All that remains is to clean up the graduating tool and screw it all together. It can be cleaned with a piece of emery paper on a stick,

Below *The graduating tool before the handle is screwed in position.*

The tool post having the finishing touches put to it. This process is known as engine turning; a piece of wooden dowel, fixed into the chuck of the bench drill, is covered in fine grinding paste, and continually brought into contact with the surface of the work while the drill is rotating. The finished result can be seen on the photographs of the completed tool. It is a very pleasing and professional looking effect achieved with the minimum of effort.

or with a fine file to leave a nice smooth finish. However, I did not do mine that way for two reasons. Firstly, I think that the tools look better with some variation in the finish. Secondly, I am quite sure that there is a danger of getting a slight curvature on the edges of the base if done in that way. I scraped my base with a small scraper, although a file with a ground-off edge would have done just as well. It could as easily have been dealt with in the same way as the tool post; held in the drill vice and worked over with a grinding paste and a piece of wooden dowel. The result is a pleasing finish which does not rust as easily as straight-grained work.

6 A KNURLING TOOL

There is no mystery about knurling. It is the process of cutting a pattern on a metal object, either as a means of providing a grip, or just as a form of decoration. In model engineering, where we use much lighter equipment, we need to take care which type of knurling tool is used, in order to avoid damage to the lathe. As the

The finished knurling tool. This type of construction stops the tendency for the arms to move sideways, which can happen with many types causing uneven knurling. The disadvantage, however, is that this tool will not completely close up, but it is suitable for most applications in model engineering and has the advantage of extreme simplicity of construction.

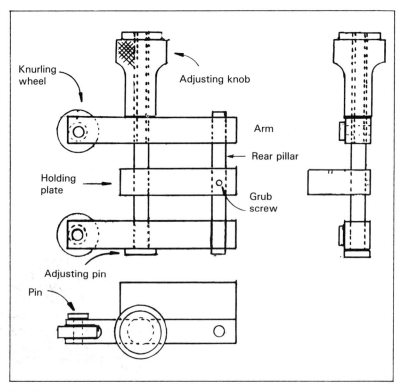

Fig 21 *General construction details.*

process consists of forcing a pre-cut hardened wheel into the
metal, it follows that quite a considerable amount of pressure is
needed. The harder the metal to be knurled, the greater the
pressure that we have to apply. Careful design of the knurling tool
can go a long way towards helping the process and preventing
damage to the lathe.

If we were to put a single knurling wheel into a suitably shaped
holder and mount it in the lathe toolpost, the wheel could be
wound into the work whilst it is rotating and the pattern of that
wheel would then be cut into the metal. Usually we need the
knurled pattern to be wider than the wheel itself, so not only is it
wound into the metal but it is also drawn along it. If we are
working on soft material such as brass and the knurling is to be
very fine, there is no problem, but if, however, we are working on,
say, steel and want a deep pattern, then the forces set up are quite
capable of damaging the lathe bearings. To obviate this, as often
as possible we should use a knurling tool that has two wheels
which work with a caliper action. By closing the calipers, the
forces are taken by the tool itself rather than the lathe bearings,
although there will still be some strain on the lathe. Because this
type of tool is commonly used, manufacturers not only provide

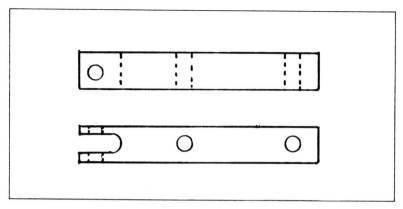

Fig 22 *Arms (two off)*.

single knurling wheels, but also make them to work in pairs. It should also be remembered that when knurling takes place, a great deal of heat is set up and so a cutting liquid should always be used.

Having discussed the operation, let us now proceed with making the tool (Figure 21). We must first acquire our knurling wheels. These will have to be purchased, and unless the tool is being made for a particularly big lathe then I would suggest you obtain the smallest pair possible. Usually these are ⅝in outside diameter and ³⁄₁₆in wide and have a bore of ¼in. There may be some made with metric measurements but at the time of writing I have never seen any, or indeed any reference to them in tool stockists catalogues. The wheels are purchased as a pair, left and right handed, and in a variety of patterns to your own choice.

The wheels are supported on arms and for these we will need two identical pieces of mild steel bar (Figure 22). I used a square section but if the wheels are on the thick side, a rectangular section would be better. The wheels I used, by the way, were of the dimensions quoted above, so the arms were about ½in (12mm) square and some 2¼in (60mm) long. Cover two opposite sides of one with marking blue and, with odd leg calipers, scribe a line centrally along each side and mark three hole positions on one side. The rear one, which takes a round metal bar, should be some ³⁄₁₆in (5mm) from the end at the outer edge of its circumference; the central one should be about 1¼in (30mm) from the rear one and the third will form the end of the slot to accommodate the knurling wheel. Therefore, before drilling it, the side of the bar should be marked out for the hole that will take the pin for the knurling wheel. A measurement can then be taken back from this for the third hole to form a slot which will allow the knurling wheels to clear the bar when fitted. When the holes are all marked out, drill a pilot hole through each with a small drill, say ⅛in (3mm), and file off the burrs.

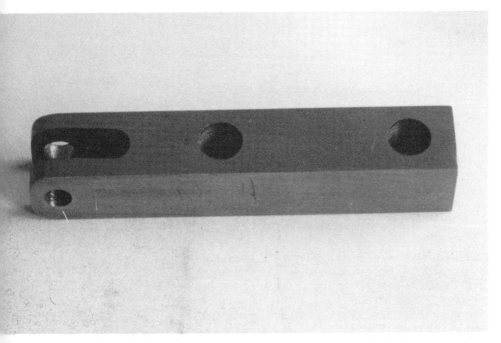

The slotted end of the arm takes the knurling wheel. A short counterbore on the centre holes provides a recess for the spring and allows the wheels to close together more.

Mark out the hole for the knurling wheel pin on the second bar and pilot drill it as above, then, using our old friend the cyanoacrylic adhesive, stick the drilled bar to the second one, and, when set, use it as a guide to drill the required holes in the other bar. The bars can then be separated by putting one in a vice and tapping the side of the other, using either a hammer and a block of wood or a copper mallet. When this has been done, the three holes in line can be opened out to their finished sizes. The rear and centre ones are to take suitable bars of round material, and I would suggest ³⁄₁₆in (5mm) if the bars' sizes are as I suggested. If they are larger, then use a proportionally larger drill. The hole at the front will need to be opened out into a slot to clear the width of the knurling wheels. The holes for the knurl pins can be left until later before receiving their final treatment.

To convert the holes at the front into slots, either use a hacksaw or, if you have a slitting saw, this can be used fitted to a suitable mandrel in the lathe. Slitting saws are always worth the investment; they are comparatively cheap, last for ages and are perfect for short cuts which need to be absolutely straight. The mandrel needs only to be a piece of bar turned to a step the size of the bore of the saw and then threaded to hold the saw in position with a large nut.

Above *Drilling the first arm for the knurling tool, which will be used as a guide for drilling the second arm*

Below *The arms of the knurling tool are held together with adhesive to allow precise location of the holes taking the knurling wheel securing pins.*

Above *The slot in the arm being cut with a slitting saw mounted in the lathe. With a little care, the job can also be done just as effectively with an ordinary hacksaw.*

Below *The pins which hold the knurling wheels in position — note the small bronze bearings inset in the wheels. If these are omitted the pins will have to be hardened otherwise they will wear out with the first application of the tool.*

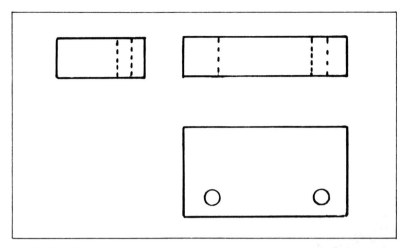

Fig 23 *Holding plate.*

The pin holes can now be dealt with and we need a clearance hole on one side of the slot and a tapped one on the other. The sizes will depend on your knurling wheels and here we have another decision to make. Knurling wheels are so hard that if you mount them directly on to steel pins, they will cut through them in seconds. My solution to this was to put tiny bronze bushes which are a 'push' fit into the bores of the wheels. Another solution would be to make the pins of silver steel and harden them, but the advantage of using bushes is that the diameter of the pins is reduced and this means that the arms can be made of smaller section than would otherwise be necessary.

The central bar of metal, the holding plate (Figure 23) is a flat mild steel section. It must be of suitable thickness to fit into your tool post and wide enough to be clamped into it firmly. The bar I used was the same thickness as the arms and just over twice as wide. The lengths will again have to be set according to the tool being made, but the photographs and drawings will give some idea of how long it should be. It will need to be temporarily fixed with adhesive to one of the bars and drilled through so that the two holes correspond with those in the arms. A small hole can then be drilled and tapped dissecting the rear hole ready for a grub screw that will hold the rear pillar in position.

The pins for the knurling wheels are straightforward turning jobs, only threaded as far as necessary to hold in the threaded side of the slot. The head should be kept fairly thin, but not so thin as to destroy the strength; I would suggest ⅛in (3mm).

The adjusting pin (Figure 21) is again a straightforward turning job with a thread on the end to allow the knob to be tightened up. The head should be somewhat thicker than the heads of the knurling wheel pins, and the pin itself is of a larger diameter to allow it to take the forces imposed when tightening up the tool.

The adjusting pin and knob. The two short springs are also shown.

The knob at the top should be turned to shape, drilled and tapped, and then finally knurled to provide a gripping surface. Assuming that no knurling tool is available, the knob could be left until the tool is completed and the tool itself used for knurling it by tightening the pin temporarily with any suitable ordinary nut and spanner. In that way, we can make the tool work for itself! The shape of the knob is entirely up to the individual and the drawing is there only as a suggestion. The thread used on this and the adjusting pin is again a matter of individual choice but try not to make it less than $\frac{3}{16}$in (5mm) as there is too much strain involved in the operation for a smaller thread.

The metal bar that goes through at the rear needs no description; it is simply a length of round steel bar. It is locked in a central position by the grub screw. Finally, when the tool is assembled, two short lengths of spring are placed on the adjusting pin to allow the tool to open on its own when the knob is turned. The tool can be encouraged to close up a little more to knurl an even smaller workpiece if the arms are slightly counterbored, to allow the spring to nestle inside. Do not go too deep with this or the strength of the arms will be impaired.

7 A RADIUSING TOOL

This little tool will enable the constructor to turn inside and outside radii on work held centrally to the lathe mandrel. Without such a tool this is a far from easy operation and most methods that I know of tend to end up with the radius having a flat at the end. The principle of the tool is very straightforward. An adjustable tool post can be moved to either side of the tool's central axis and depending on whether this axis is in front or behind the cutting edge of the tool, will decide whether the radius is concave or convex. The adjustment capability allows various radii to be turned with a good degree of accuracy. The tool is particularly useful when making machinery or when making such items as governors or round knobs, and is absolutely essential for any form of ornamental turning. No doubt readers will soon find many uses for it.

The tool consists of a rigid base mounted on the cross slide; it may either be round as in the photograph, or square as in the drawings, depending on the material to hand. It is, however, far

The finished radiusing tool showing the locking screws which are on one side only.

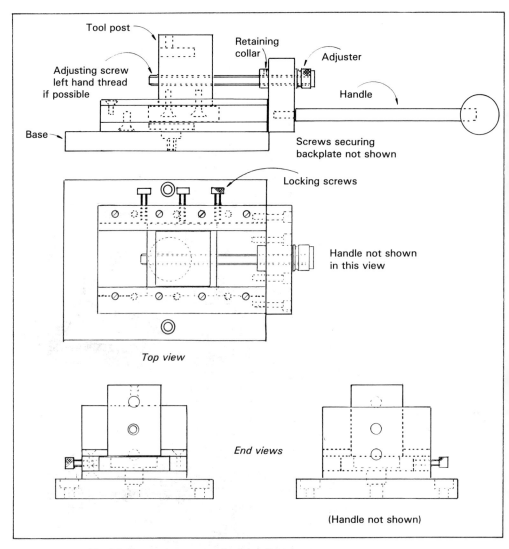

Fig 24 *General construction details.*

more likely that there will be a piece of square flat plate in the scrap box than a round piece as I have used and it is for this reason that the drawings are shown that way. The round base may look better, I suppose, and so, if any readers wish to, there is no reason why they should not turn some flat stock circular. If they do so I would suggest that it be drilled first and it can then be held on a screwed mandrel for completion.

It will be seen there are three holes in the base (Figure 25). One is central and the others are on either side of this. These latter two holes are for fixing the base to the cross slide and as such have to

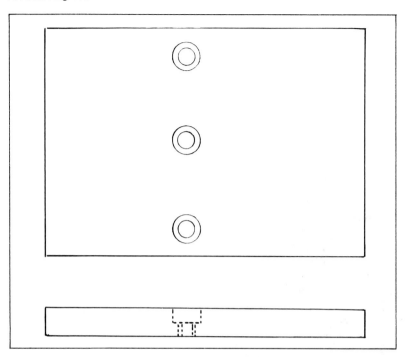

Above Fig 25 *Base.*

Below *The base, in this case circular. Note the counter bored holes for the retaining bolts. The centre hole could also be counter bored to take part of the bush if required; otherwise the bush can be entirely located in the swivel plate.*

be counterbored so that allen-headed cap screws can be used for securing. This will allow the swivel plate to be rotated over the top of the screw heads, which is essential to the operation of the tool. The holes, particularly the central one, should be drilled with the metal held in the lathe chuck to ensure that they are square as drilling machines have a nasty habit of drilling holes at an angle. The central hole can be slightly counterbored to take part of the bush that will be used to prevent wear, and the remainder should be tapped to a suitable size. For those making the device for a lathe such as a Myford ML7, a thread about ⅜in (10mm) will be ideal. For the smaller lathes, such as a Toyo 210 or a Cowells, then possibly ¼in (6mm) will be the right size. As usual, it will depend on what the constructor has available in his or her workshop, but it should be borne in mind that some strength will be needed as this thread will take all the strain when turning operations are carried out.

The swivel plate (Figure 26) is a piece of flat mild steel not less than a ¼in (6mm) thick for the larger sized lathes; ³⁄₁₆in (5mm) will do for the smaller ones. It should be drilled in the lathe and counterbored to take the large head of the swivel pin; this operation will have to be carried out with a boring tool. Three holes are then drilled along each side and countersunk. As screws will pass through these, the initial drilling should be with a tapping sized drill, then opening out to clearance size after the matching

Fig 26 *Swivel plate.*

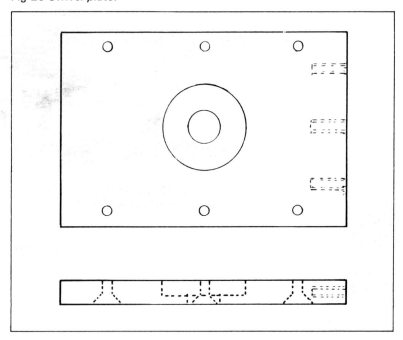

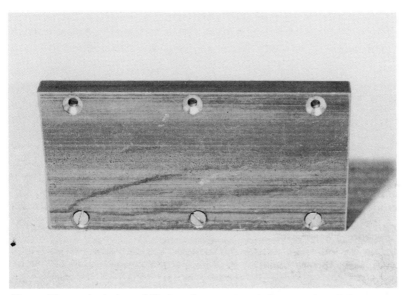

Above *The swivel plate drilled and countersunk from underneath to take the slide bars.*

Below *Boring the swivel plate for the large pin head.*

Above *The swivel base of the radiusing tool showing the counterbored hole to take the screw head and the bush.*

Below Fig 27 *Slide bar.*

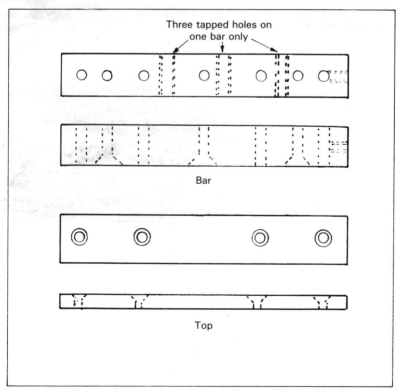

Three tapped holes on
one bar only

Bar

Top

holes have been drilled. There are also three holes in the end of the swivel plate, but these should be left until the rear or end plate is made.

The slide bars (Figure 27) consist of two parts. The lower section, which will be attached to the swivel plate, will be of a square or flat material of the same thickness as that used to make the runner. At this point, the runner can be cut to size to act as a guide for positioning the lower parts of the slide bars, which should be stuck in position, using a cyanoacrylic adhesive, on the swivel plate and allow to dry. When well set, drill through the swivel plate from underneath and into the slide bars. These holes can either pass right through or be left blind. Do not at this point remove the slide bars from the swivel base.

The top surfaces of the slide bars should now be marked out, drilled and countersunk. Stick them to the lower slide bars and, when set, drill through. Again, at this stage, the holes should all be drilled to tapping size. When these operations are complete, run the clearance drill through the four holes in each slide bar top and

One of the slide bars on the swivel plate. This clearly indicates the method of building up the slide bars by drilling and tapping from either side. At this point the hole for the pivot pin has not been drilled or counterbored.

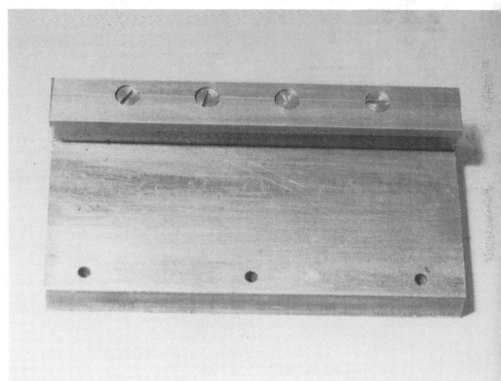

The completed swivel plate and slide bars. The screw holes will be filled and the assembly painted to keep rust away, and to make it easier to clean.

the three in each side of the base. If you wish, at this point, the components can be broken apart, but personally I prefer to keep them stuck together and in that way I use both screws and adhesive to mate the parts. When the tapping is completed screw up tight with countersunk screws, making sure that the heads are below the metal surfaces of the slide bar tops.

Finally, the side of one of the slide bars will need three tapped holes. These are for locking screws with which to tighten up the runner and tool post when using the finished device. The position of the holes is not important as long as one screw will be able to be nipped up on the runner, whatever the position of the tool. Brass knurled screws will prevent nasty little score marks appearing on the runner when the tool is in use.

The rear plate for the adjuster (Figure 28) should be made next. The two larger holes should be drilled first. One of these takes the adjusting thread and the other the handle. The method of securing the handle is a matter for the constructor; it can either be screwed in or held with a retaining compound. Personally, I prefer the latter method these days, although one advantage of screwing it in position would be to enable the radiusing tool to be stored more easily by removing the handle.

The five smaller holes can now be drilled. These are for the securing screws that hold the rear plate to the swivel plate and slide bars. They should be positioned so that the bottom three will go into the swivel plate and the other two into the slide bars. After the holes have been drilled in the plate, hold it to the swivel plate assembly with the adhesive and, when dry, drill through. The rear plate can then be opened out and counterbored to take allen-headed cap screws whilst the mating holes in the swivel plate and slide bars are tapped to suit.

The runner (Figure 29) has two holes drilled along a centre line to secure it to the tool post (Figure 30) of which it is, of course, the base. Use adhesive to secure the tool post to the runner, then

Right Fig 28 *Rear plate.*

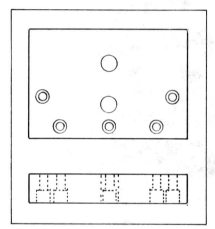

Below Fig 29 *Runner.*

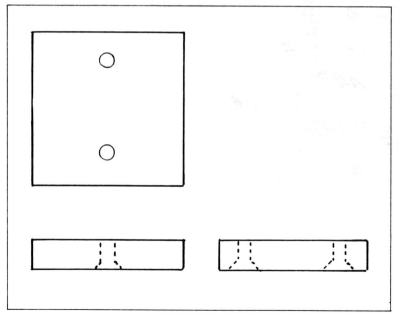

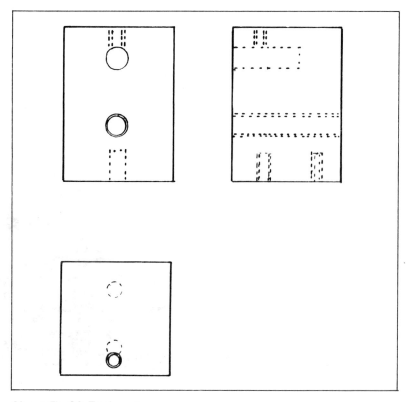

Above Fig 30 *Tool post.*

Below *The tool post and runner assembly. The hole will either have to be tapped to take the adjusting screw or drilled oversize to take a suitably tapped bush. The hole for the tool bit is drilled after locating the correct position for it by using a scriber secured in the lathe chuck. The overall height of the tool post can also be adjusted at this stage if required.*

place the tool post assembly between the slide bars. The fit should be such that it will slide in and out without noticeable wobble.

Clamp the tool post to the rear plate and drill through the hole that will take the adjuster thread. If the runner has been made slightly longer than the tool post, then a small packing piece should be added for this operation. Some readers may prefer to spot the hole in the tool post and then drill it away from the rest of the job. The tapped hole in the tool post is shown as a direct hole on the drawings. This is because if much use is anticipated it will be better to open out the hole and make a threaded brass or bronze bush secured in the tool post with retaining compound. Such a bush will not wear quite so quickly and also can always be replaced if necessary. The thread should, if possible, be left-handed as this helps achieve the correct rotation on the adjuster. If you do not happen to have a left-handed tap, use a normal one and when in use remember to turn the adjuster the correct way. The thread diameter should be about ¼in (6mm) for the larger lathes and ³⁄₁₆in (5mm) for the smaller ones.

The adjuster itself is a piece of studding with a plain section where it is to be secured in the rear plate. The adjusting knob (Figure 31) is a simple turning job, being then drilled and tapped as required and then held in position with retaining compound. The other end of the plain section taken a small collar (Figure 32) held in position with a grub screw. You may find that a washer on either side of the rear plate will help to make things run smoothly. I made my washers of PTFE, which, being a self-lubricating plastic, gave a really nice easy movement, but brass or even steel will do if you do not have any PTFE.

So far so good, but the tool is not going to work unless it has

Fig 31 *Adjusting knob.*   Fig 32 *Collar.*

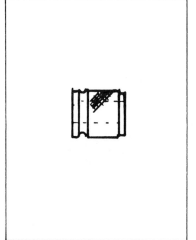
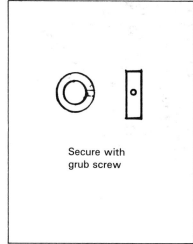

Secure with grub screw

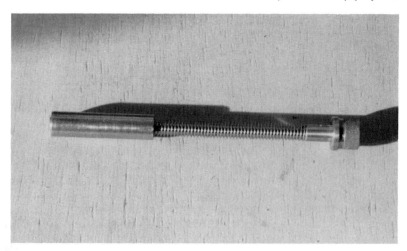

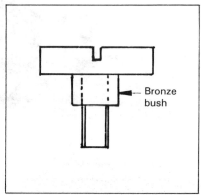

— Bronze bush

Above *Adjuster screw assembly. The thread is shown located in the tapped bush. The plain section will go through the rear plate and the collar is secured to this with a grub screw, allowing the screw to rotate but not move in any other direction.*

Left Fig 33 *Pivot pin.*

Below *Pivot pin with bronze or brass bush. The large head is essential to take the thrust put on the tool when in use. The bush reduces wear and simplifies replacement.*

The radiusing attachment being used for turning the top of a locomotive chimney.

something on which to swivel, the obvious thing being a pivot pin (Figure 33). The head should be quite large in order to counteract the lifting forces applied to the tool when in use. A slot should then be made across the diameter with a hack saw to allow the screw to be tightened up in the base. A brass or bronze bush is needed to fit over the swivel pin and into the counterbore in the swivel block and base. This will prevent too much wear, and again can easily be replaced, whereas worn parts on the tool itself would create difficulties with such maintenance.

Finally, assemble the tool and mount it on the cross slide of the lathe. Tighten up one of the securing screws on the slide bars so that the tool post is held absolutely rigid. Place a scriber in the lathe chuck and wind the cross slide in, so that the scriber makes a mark across the tool post. Dismantle and use this mark to drill the hole required for the tool. Cross drill and tap to take a grub screw for securing the tool in position.

That is all there is to the construction of this most useful radiusing tool. The operation of it is simple enough. The size of the radius is altered by winding the adjusting screw in or out. The shape is created by pulling the handle round while the work is revolving in the lathe. Remember, though, that such a tool can only be used successfully by making comparatively light cuts, so take it easy when using it.

If you like, the first job can be to make the round knob to fit on the end of the handle. I must confess here to using a plastic one which I already had in stock but, if you do decide to make one, first drill and tap the metal or plastic from which you are going to make it.

8 A VERTICAL SLIDE

This is by far the largest object described in this book, although this does not mean that it is any more complicated or difficult to make; there is just more of it, so it will take longer to make than the other projects.

First of all, why do we need a vertical slide anyway? The answer to that is that there are times when it is necessary to reverse the more normal method of lathework by using a cutting tool in the lathe chuck and we need some means of mounting the work on the cross slide which can provide additional movement; milling and fly cutting are typical examples. Even if a milling machine is available, there is still sometimes a need to carry out such operations on the lathe, if possible. Using a vertical slide enables us to adjust the height of the work on the cross slide and so, instead of running around trying to find packing to bring it up to the right height, we can just wind it up to wherever we want it and with considerable accuracy, too. It cannot, of course, be used for heavy milling work, whether it is a home-made or commercially manufactured example. The very form of construction of a vertical slide means that it can only carry out light work.

A commercial vertical slide is invariably a very narrow affair. Frequently this will mean that the work has a large overhang leading to considerable loss of rigidity. By making our own slide it is possible to provide one that can be virtually the length of the cross slide, thus giving a much greater area with which to support the work. Technically speaking, the one I am about to describe is to an extremely basic design. However, this has meant simplicity which is important. The fact that the whole thing is just screwed together means that no special equipment is needed, and it is capable of doing the job.

We obviously need to start with the base (Figure 35), upon which will depend the quality and strength of the finished slide. A piece of mild steel plate is required, roughly the same size as your cross slide, unless, that is, your lathe is one with a long cross slide, in which case to cover the whole length would not be practical. In the latter case, I would suggest that the metal should

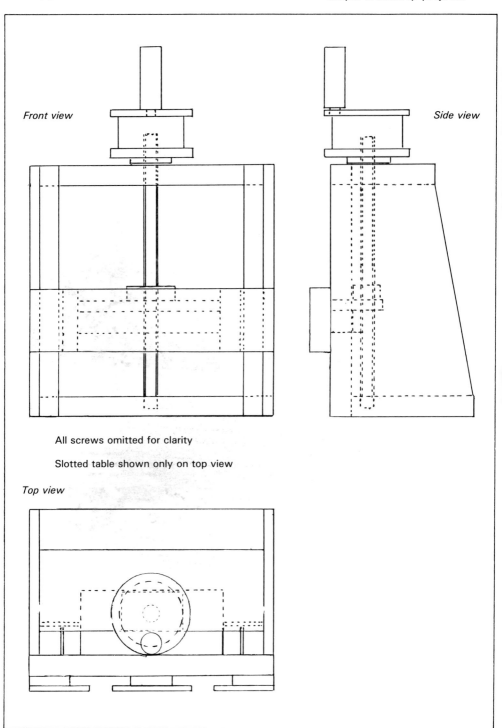

Front view

Side view

All screws omitted for clarity

Slotted table shown only on top view

Top view

Above *The finished vertical slide. The only other work that can now be carried out is to fill all the holes and smooth them off. This offers no practical advantages but does improve the appearance.*

Left Fig 34 *General construction details.*

be about two-thirds of the length of the cross slide. It must be at least 1in (25mm) thick for a lathe of about 3in centre height, and even if made for the smaller lathe, the thickness must not be less than ¾in (18mm). This thickness is very important in order to retain rigidity. Having selected suitable steel, the ends must be

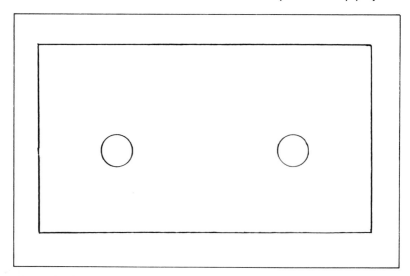

Above Fig 35 *Base.*

Below Fig 36 *Top plate.*

squared off and the best way to do this is to bolt it, end on, to the cross slide of the lathe. Check that it is absolutely square to the cross slide, and then fly cut it so that it will be not only square across the width but also across the thickness. Securing it to the cross slide may present problems on some lathes if using clamps. It may, therefore, at this stage be as well to drill the two holes that will be used to secure it to the lathe when finished, and then to bolt through these. If they should be too wide apart for the metal to be bolted across the slide, drill a third hole. This will always be handy if the vertical slide is to be fitted in a different position at some time, and will certainly do no harm anyway. The position of these holes will obviously have to be arranged to suit your own lathe cross slide.

Fig 37 *Uprights.*

The next part we need is the top plate (Figure 36) and this must be of *exactly* the same length as the base. It need only be about two-thirds of the width, but it *must* be of at least two-thirds of the thickness. It should be clearly understood that light material will just not do for either of these parts. The top should then be machined square in the same way as the base. If it is possible to drill it so that both the base and the top can be squared up as one, you can be absolutely sure that it will be right.

We next need two pieces of bar to act as the runners or uprights for the sliding table itself (Figure 37). Some care in selecting these will be required. The thickness must be slightly less than that chosen for the runners on the table and the reason for this will become obvious when you start making the slide. The uprights should be good hefty pieces of material. On my vertical slide (shown in the illustrations) they were made from $7/16$ square steel strip since it just happened that some was available. It would have been better to use metal of the same thickness but twice as wide, as this would have helped with rigidity. A hole should then be drilled at each end and they must be positioned identically on each, to ensure squareness when the finished project is assembled.

These holes in the uprights should then be used as a guide for drilling tapping sized holes in the top and the base so that they can all be bolted together. I used round-headed screws for temporary assembly and then countersunk the holes later and fitted hexagon socket screws so that I could get the extra torque when tightening up.

Assembly of the base, top and two uprights.

The side plates (Figure 38) can be pieces of either mild steel plate or, as in my case, alloy, but whichever material you choose it should be nice and thick. For the size of vertical slide I am describing, the sides should be at least ¼in (6mm) thick and even for small lathes at least ³⁄₁₆in (5mm). The sides, of course, help to keep things rigid and that is why thick material is so important. They should be cut to shape as shown in the drawing and then marked out and drilled. Do not try and skimp on the number of holes as the screws themselves again all help with the overall strength of the finished job. The holes should be countersunk and then the sides clamped in position on the frame consisting of the top, base and uprights. Drill through the sides into the top and base when you are absolutely certain that everything is nice and square.

It is then a case of tapping all the holes and screwing things together (Figure 39). If this work has been carefully carried out, everything should end up square and rigid with no need for any further support. If things have not gone according to plan, later on pieces of angle can be set into the joints and bolted in position. A word of warning here, should this be necessary. Do not rely on the

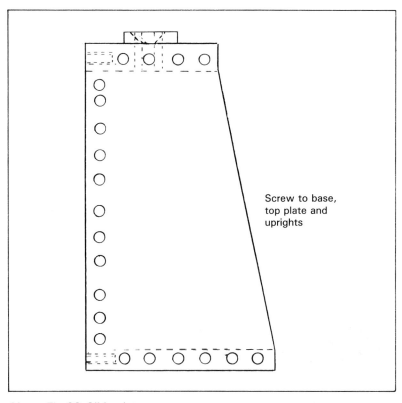

Screw to base,
top plate and
uprights

Above Fig 38 *Slide plate.*

Below *To drill the uprights it will be necessary first to locate the side plates (which have already been drilled) with a pair of clamps. The operation can then be carried out in one go.*

The main frame being prepared for drilling.

angles being square, for they very rarely are. Put each piece in the four-jaw chuck and face the sides of the angles lightly so that you make sure all is well.

We now need to start on the table (Figure 40). It is not necessary for this to have tee slots although in the illustrations and drawings I have shown how they can be made. A good strong plain table will do the job quite well since this can be drilled and tapped to take your machine vice or any other holding device you may be using; it will still work just as well and you will save yourself a lot of work. However, for those who do want to make tee slots, the instructions are given at the end of the text, although they will need to be fixed into place before completing the rear of the table.

The table must be machined to length, whether slotted or not. The method described previously of bolting it to the cross slide of the lathe and machining it with a fly-cutter is the best way to do

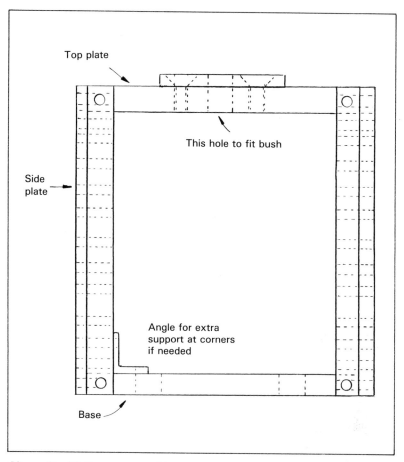

Top plate

This hole to fit bush

Side plate

Angle for extra
support at corners
if needed

Base

Above Fig 39 *Frame assembly.*

Below Fig 40 *Table (shown without tee slots).*

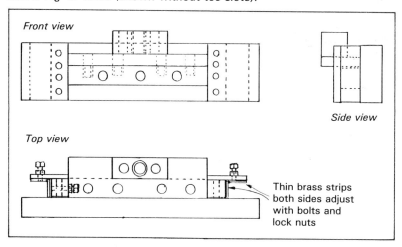

Front view

Side view

Top view

Thin brass strips
both sides adjust
with bolts and
lock nuts

The underside of the table after drilling operations have been carried out for the tee slots. The guide bar has been drilled and is now secured on the back of the table with adhesive ready for further drilling operations.

this. There are three pieces of metal bolted to the back of the table, as shown in the drawings. Two are upright to act as guides on the vertical sides of the frame, and the other heftier piece will hold the nut that takes the lead screw. I first of all drilled these and stuck them in position with cyanoacrylic adhesive in the usual way. There are also brass rubbing strips on the uprights and these were put in position to help obtain the correct location when the pieces were offered up to the frame of the slide, which has already been described.

The vertical members of the table will have to be slightly thicker than the runners on the frame to allow for these brass rubbing strips. Here we see why I used $7/16$in, as it enables me to use $1/2$in (12mm) square material to make the vertical pieces, allowing $1/16$in (1.5mm) brass strips to fit. A similar combination will be needed whatever size slide you are making.

The next operation is to drill right through the table and bolt these uprights in position. Good sturdy bolts were used here as they will be taking all the strain.

A piece of plate is now bolted across each of the vertical bars that have been secured to the back of the table to prevent the table from moving forward when operated. Brass gib strips will be used to take up any play and screw holes are required for the adjusting screws for these strips. Note that the brass strips on the vertical sections are only adjustable on one side, the other being secured to the upright with cyanoacrylic adhesive to retain it permanently in position.

The only other work required on the rear of the table at this stage is to drill, tap and screw on the metal bar that will take the lead screw. This will run in a specially-made nut, so the clearance hole for it can be oversize to allow some adjustment on assembly.

The lead screw (Figure 41) should ideally be a left-handed thread and making this on a lathe is not so difficult as it sounds. Simply run the machine in the normal direction but start the tool at the end near the chuck and work towards the tailstock, with the lead screw running in reverse. A square thread would be preferable and a parting tool can be used to cut it. The nut in which the lead screw runs can be made in a similar fashion but using an internal cutting tool. To prevent excessive wear, the nut should be made of brass or alloy. To finish off, the nut should be tapped to clean out the thread. To do this you will need to make your own tap and therefore I suggest that free-cutting silver steel is used for the lead screw and a short length of this can then be cut off to make the tap as shown on the illustration. Obviously this will mean making the lead screw overlength in the first place. A

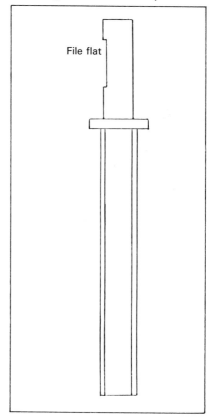

File flat

Fig 41 *Lead screw.*

Above *An extra length of lead screw has been turned from silver steel and threaded. A relief and cutting edge is then formed with a file, after which it is hardened and tempered, and used as a tap to clean out the thread in the nut.*

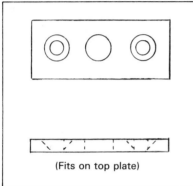

(Fits on top plate)

Left Fig 42 *Bush holder.*

cutting angle must then be placed on the piece that has been cut off, together with a flute. We only need the one flute as this tap is only for cleaning out the thread after machining. Finally, harden the tap and then you are ready for this final cleaning out operation.

For those who do not fancy cutting the thread in their lathe or perhaps do not have the facilities to do so, an ordinary coarse thread will do the job. It should be as coarse as possible and, in fact, if you cut your own, aim at about eight or ten threads per inch, or a pitch of 2 to 2.5mm. The main problem with using an ordinary right-handed thread is that the slide will move upwards when the handle is screwed inwards. I am quite sure, however, that once you get used to the idea of turning it in the opposite direction you will not notice the difference.

The nut in which the lead screw runs is bolted to the back of the table, a hole will have to be drilled in the metal bar that holds the nut for the screw to pass through. I would suggest making the holes in either the plate or the nut slightly oval so that some adjustment can be made on final assembly. The top of the lead screw, which is plain, can also run in a plate, preferably with a bush to prevent wear (Figure 42). This plate can again be bolted to the top of the vertical slide and once more slight ovality will allow some adjustment.

Above *The nut for the lead screw, bolted to the back of the table. By making the clearance holes for the screw slightly oval at both the nut and the top bush, some adjustment is available to line up the lead screw.*

Below *The steel plate which carries the bronze bush for the top of the lead screw, bolted to the top of the slide.*

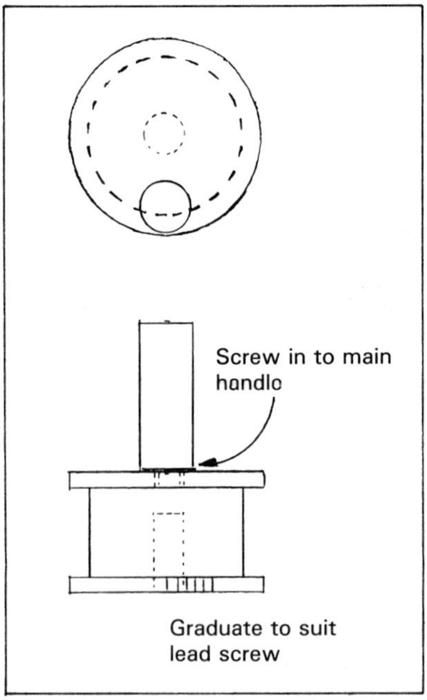

Fig 43 *Handle.*

The handle and lead screw dial (Figure 43) are straightforward turning jobs and the design is largely a matter for the individual. Graduations should be put round the edge (see illustration in Chapter Six) and a mark made with a chisel on the top of the vertical slide for lining them up. The handle should be held in position on the lead screw using a suitable grub screw.

As far as the actual vertical slide is concerned that is all there is to its construction. Apart from the fact that it does need care to ensure that it is both rigid and accurately put together, it is no great problem for anyone to make.

The tee slotted table is built up from pieces of flat mild steel plate and probably the photographs show how this is done as well as any explanation I can give. It is a case of building up the bottom part of the tee slots first, by the usual method of fixing with adhesive, then drilling, tapping and countersinking. The top part of the tees are made in the same way. Metal or wooden bars of the chosen width should be used to act as spacers when sticking both bottom and top plates in position. It is also a good idea to cut the table to length after assembling the tee slots in case things do not work out correctly. After completing the tee slots, we are left with a table with a number of recesses where the countersunk heads of the screws are situated but these can, if you wish, be filled, either with a proprietry metal filler, or with a mixture of epoxy resin and steel filings. This will certainly be done later on in the case of the one shown in the photographs. Should it be decided that tee slots are not going to be made in this way, the table must be made of

Above *The start of the table for the vertical slide, if tee slots are to be used. The first section of the bar has been screwed to the main table with countersunk screws. The heads of these must be below the level of the metal to allow the second part of the tee to be screwed on.*

Below *Having put the first section in place, a suitably sized bar of metal is used as a spacer, and then a layer of adhesive is applied to secure the second pre-drilled plate whilst the main table is drilled.*

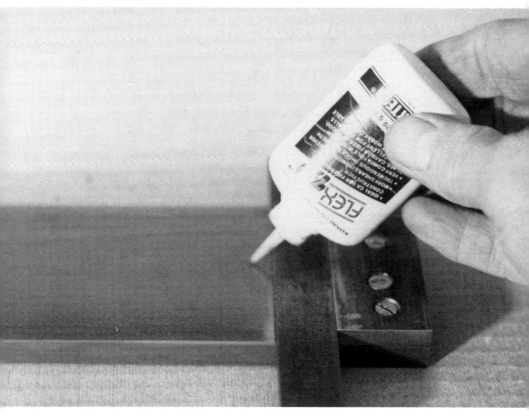

Above *The second plate is now in position ready for drilling the table. Note that at this stage a tapping sized drill is used and later this is opened out for clearance and countersink.*

Below *The table begins to take shape with four plates now in position.*

Above *The top plates for the tee slots are located in the same way as the bottom ones. Pre-drilled plates are stuck in position as drilling guides and a suitable bar of material is again used as a spacer.*

Below *The front of the tee slotted table ready for work on the back. When the table is completed, the countersinks can be filled with a mixture of epoxy adhesive and iron filings, and when set, this can be smoothed over. Alternatively, one of the proprietary metal fillers could be used.*

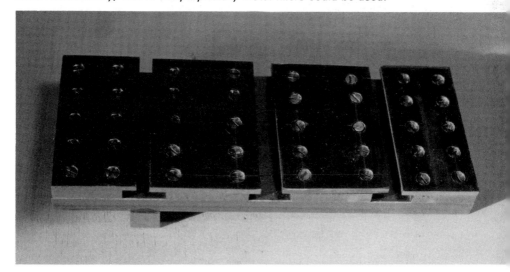

The construction of the completed vertical slide from the rear.

thicker material to give it strength. I would suggest a minimum of
¾in (18mm) for the larger sized lathes and ½in (12mm) for the
smaller ones.

Of course, if you have the necessary facilities, a table can be
made up using a heavy metal plate and milling out the tee slots,
but that is a matter for the individual with the luxury of such
equipment and is beyond the scope of this book.

9 *A SINGLE-CYCLINDER OSCILLATING STEAM ENGINE*

The oscillating steam engine is probably the simplest form of steam engine that it is possible to build, although there have been claims for other types being even simpler. It is certainly the easiest type of engine to understand and for this reason is an excellent choice of model for anyone wishing to learn about steam engine construction. In most forms of engine, there is a closed cylinder in which a piston moves backwards and forwards. A valve is opened to allow the expanding element being used to drive the piston to enter the cylinder. When that material is spent, another valve opens to allow it to be exhausted. In the case of our car engines, the element is a mixture of petrol and air which, when ignited, causes it to explode and drive the piston. In the case of a steam engine, because steam expands there is no need for it to be exploded and that expansion force above will drive the piston.

All that is needed, then, is the closed cylinder, the piston and the two valves. in the case of the oscillating engine, the cylinder itself forms part of the valves and there is no need to construct separate ones. The cylinder is pivoted about halfway along its length and this allows the cylinder to rock or oscillate on the pivot. A hole in the top of the cylinder matches up with one in the port face — the name for the point where the steam is introduced — and therefore the steam passes through into the cylinder under pressure from the boiler. It then expands thus driving the piston down. As the piston rod turns the crank, the cylinder tilts on its pivot, and when it has tilted the maximum amount allowed by the crank to which the piston rod is attached, another hole in the port face lines up with the one at the top of the cylinder, thus allowing the steam to escape. At this point, the piston is already on its way back up having been carried there by the momentum of a flywheel. At the top of the stroke the cylinder has again tilted and steam is once more allowed in, and so the cycle goes on. Having built a single-cylinder engine, the principle will become obvious and, once it has been mastered, anyone can easily design and build their own engine.

It will be seen from the drawings that I have given

General view showing the steam connection, and the pivot with spring and securing nut. The fly wheel is held in position with a small screw.

measurements for the steam engines. I have done so because the models are designed to be made on a lathe of almost any size and so the measurements will apply whichever lathe they are made on, unlike the tools, the sizes of which had to be adapted for the various machine tools with which they were to be used.

We start by making the cylinder (Figure 45) for which we will require a piece of ½in (12mm) square brass bar. It should be

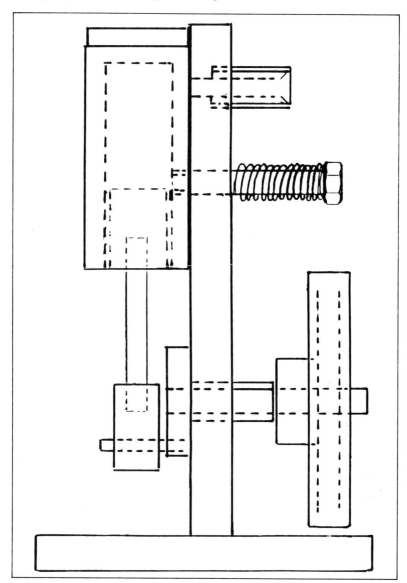

Fig 44 *General construction details.*

centred in the four-jaw chuck and a ⁵⁄₁₆in (8mm) bore drilled right
through. I say drilled, but it is preferable really if the hole is reamed
to size, as the better the fit of the piston, the better the operation
of the engine. If a suitable reamer is not available then a D-bit can
be made to the right size and that will do almost as well.

Having bored the cylinder, we now need to make two small
holes centrally along one side of it as shown in the drawing (Figure
46). One hole is ¹⁄₁₆in (1.5mm) diameter for the steam port, the

other, for the pivot, should be drilled tapping size for a 5BA, or 3mm, thread. This latter hole will almost certainly have to be drilled right through into the bore, otherwise there will be insufficient depth of metal to cut a long enough thread. This will not matter, although the bore will have to be cleaned out again after tapping to get rid of the swarf created by the drilling and tapping. The smaller hole should go right through into the cylinder bore anyway, as this is the part through which steam enters and exhausts.

Fig 45 *Cylinder and pivot pin.*

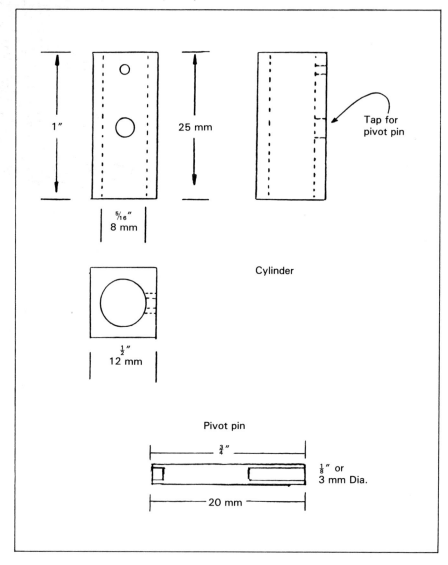

Drilling the cylinder in the four-jaw chuck. This photograph is relevant to all three engines in this and the following Projects, which basically all have the same cylinder blocks.

The next job is to make the small cap (Figure 47) that will fit on the top of the cylinder to seal one end of it. This should be made from ½in (12mm) diameter brass bar. The dimensions and shape are shown in the drawing. When finished it can be soft soldered to the top of the cylinder.

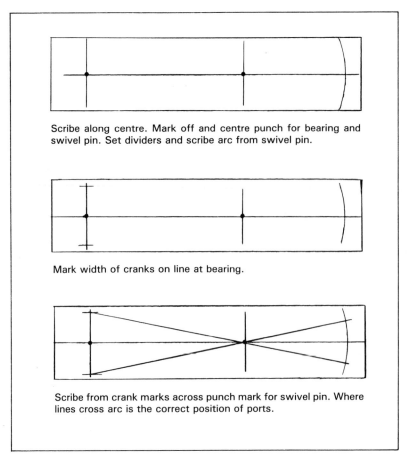

Scribe along centre. Mark off and centre punch for bearing and swivel pin. Set dividers and scribe arc from swivel pin.

Mark width of cranks on line at bearing.

Scribe from crank marks across punch mark for swivel pin. Where lines cross arc is the correct position of ports.

Above Fig 46 *Marking out steam ports.*

Below Fig 47 *Cylinder cap.*

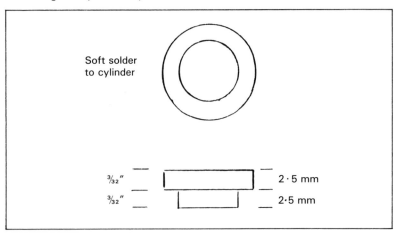

Above *The cylinder with its pivot pin. The cylinder cover is seen at the side ready for soldering into position.*

Below *The cover being soldered on to the cylinder. The cylinder block is set on bricks, then both components are fluxed and then heated with a blowlamp until a tiny blob of solder will run freely on the metal.*

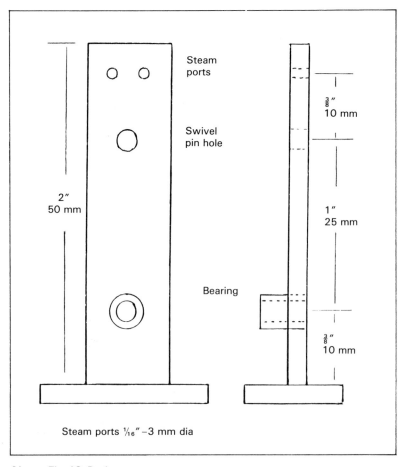

Above Fig 48 *Body.*

Below *The engine body which includes the port face. The steam and pivot holes can be clearly seen, as can the bush for the shaft. The bush is held in place with retaining compound.*

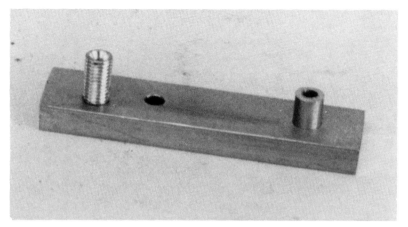

Above *The body with the steam connection and bush in position.*

Right *The body soldered to the base.*

The main body of the engine (Figure 48), which includes the port face, comes next. This is made from ⅛in (3mm) brass strip, which will need carefully marking out for the four holes that have to be drilled in it. No measurement is given for the width of the two steam parts at the top but the measurements for positioning them correctly are shown in the drawings. One of these two small holes, that for the steam inlet pipe, will need to be opened out half its length to be tapped ³⁄₁₆ x 40 tpi., or for a 5mm metric thread.

When the body has been completed, it can be soft soldered to the base, which should be a small piece of ¹⁄₁₆in (1.5mm) brass sheet, cut to size with four holes, one at each corner, for fixing the engine onto a wooden base, or into whatever it is to drive, if that should be required.

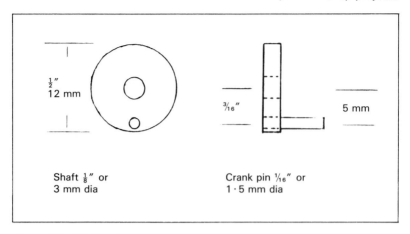

$\frac{1}{2}''$
12 mm

$\frac{3}{16}''$ 5 mm

Shaft $\frac{1}{8}''$ or
3 mm dia

Crank pin $\frac{1}{16}''$ or
1·5 mm dia

Above Fig 49 *Crank.*

Below *The crank and crank pin on the shaft. Both the crank pin and shaft are held in position with retaining compound.*

The crank (Figure 49) is a section of mild steel bar with one centrally drilled hole to take the main shaft and another smaller one drilled to take the crank pin. The crank pin is simply a piece of $\frac{1}{16}$in (1.5mm) diameter silver or mild steel. It is held in the hole in the crank with retaining compound.

The piston (Figure 50) is a piece of suitably sized brass or phosphor bronze drilled centrally to take the piston rod, and with a groove turned round the circumference to allow oil to collect when running, so as to keep it lubricated. On more advanced engines, some form of packing or piston ring would be used, but it is not necessary on this little engine.

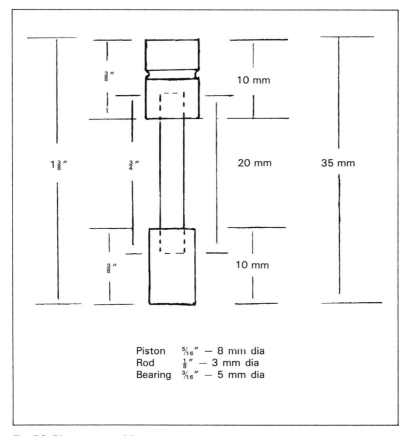

Fig 50 *Piston assembly.*

The piston rod is a piece of ⅛in (3mm) diameter stainless steel, threaded at each end as shown. A piece of brass is then drilled and tapped to fit to the end of the piston to act as the big end bearing and then this should be cross drilled to make a hole into which the crank pin fits. The piston, piston rod and the big end can now all be assembled.

The flywheel (Figure 51) can be made from steel or brass, or even aluminium if available. I used brass because I had a suitable offcut, but I would normally use steel as it is more readily available. The boss should be cross drilled 8BA, or 1.5mm, to take the set screw securing the flywheel to its crankshaft. A grub screw that passes right into the boss makes a neat job, or you can do as I did and use a short ordinary slotted screw. The bearing for the shaft is brass and is simply drilled and faced off in the lathe, and then held in place in the main body with retaining compound. The crankshaft itself is simply a length of ⅛in (3mm) diameter mild or silver steel rod.

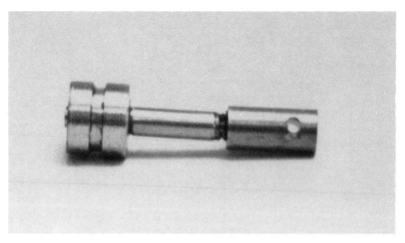

Above *The piston assembly consisting of the piston, piston rod and big end bearing. The groove in the piston is to hold oil which should always be introduced into the engine before running takes place.*

Below Fig 51 *Flywheel.*

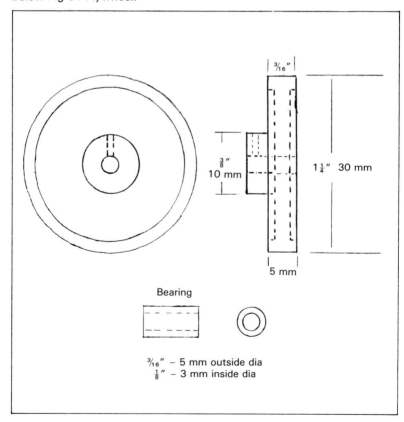

Above *The flywheel. The recessed turning is for appearance only and the wheel could be left plain if one so wished. The flywheel is applicable to the single cylinder oscillating engine as well as the piston valve engine.*

Below *A view of the engine showing the crank and the big end bearing. It also shows quite clearly how the cover is soldered to the cylinder block.*

Before assembling, turn up on the lathe a threaded brass fitting or union for the steam intake and fit this in the hole already made in the body. A stainless steel rod threaded at both ends will be required for the cylinder pivot. Make sure that when it is screwed into the side of the cylinder, it does not pass right through into the bore, otherwise in operation it will foul the piston. The swivel pin is then fitted with a spring and a retaining nut. Almost any type of circular compression spring will do, but if you do not have anything suitable to hand then a piece of 25 gauge bronze wire wound round a suitably sized steel rod held in the lathe chuck will do. Pass the end of the wire through a small hole in the piece of steel, rod, which should be near enough the same diameter as the cylinder pivot, and then coil the wire round the rod while turning the lathe chuck by hand. Keep the wire as taut as possible and by pulling it slightly towards the tailstock, it is possible to arrive at the right shape for the spring.

In operation it is possible that the engine may have to be started by spinning the flywheel by hand when steam is first introduced, but after that it should run quite happily and give no trouble. The most important part obviously is to make sure that the holes forming steam and exhaust ports are properly lined up. Apart from this factor, the construction is really very straightforward and this small engine can be used very successfully, for instance, to drive the propeller shaft in a small model boat.

10 A TWIN-CYLINDER OSCILLATING STEAM ENGINE

This twin cylinder oscillating engine is really only two of the singles just described, placed back to back, and most of the parts are either identical or very nearly so. Firstly, we will need two cylinders and two pistons, with piston rods and big ends, made in exactly the same way as those for the single, and using exactly the same measurements.

The two cylinder engine completed. Note the steam connection in the middle of the block. This is connected through holes in the block to the steam ports. There is also a connection on the opposite side for exhaust.

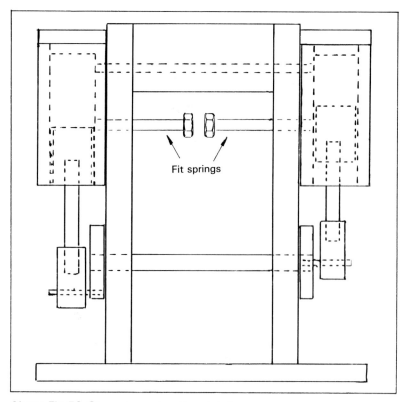

Above Fig 52 *General construction details.*

Below *To make the twin-cylinder engine two bodies are needed, both identical. They should therefore be held together with adhesive and drilled as one unit. The bottom ends can also be faced while they are held together, thus ensuring that both components are of identical length.*

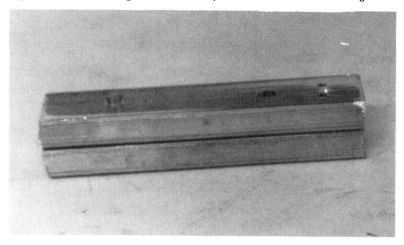

Right *To drill the two small holes for the crank pins, set a piece of steel rod through the shaft hole and hold both cranks together with a little adhesive. They can then be drilled as one and both crank pin holes will be in identical positions.*

Below *To locate the central block in position, use a piece of steel through the shaft holes so the unit is properly lined up. If it is not lined up correctly the engine will not work.*

We will also need two bodies or port faces but with a slight difference. As there is no need for separate bearings, the hole for the crank shaft can be left as the clearance size for that shaft; the double assembly will allow sufficient support since both the bodies are soldered to one base. The base is obviously slightly larger than that for the single version. The port faces in the bodies should be left as they are for the moment; there is no need to open one out and tap it to take the steam pipe, as we will see later.

We will need two cranks, but this time a small hole will have to be cross drilled across one and tapped to take a grub screw so that it can be fitted and adjusted after the shaft has been placed in position. The other crank should be fixed to the shaft with retaining compound.

The tops of the two bodies are joined together by a piece of ½in

The two bodies mounted with the central block and base soldered in position.

(12mm) square brass bar. This should be cut to a size of about 1 in (25mm) and then faced in the four-jaw chuck to ensure that it is a good square fit. It should then be carefully soft soldered in position, making sure that the solder runs right through the joints as they have to be steam tight. When this has been done, the holes for the steam distribution ports can be joined up. It is better to drill from each end until the holes meet, rather than trying to drill right through from one end to the other.

We then need to drill and tap two holes, one on either side of this top steam block. This is to take the unions for the steam and exhaust pipes, rather as we did on the back of the steam port on the single. Each hole must pass through to connect up with its steam passage. Make sure the drill does not go in too far, as the steam and exhaust passages must be kept separate.

That really is all there is to it. When it is assembled, the cranks should be set so that they are at ninety degrees to each other (it does not matter which is where). This allows the engine to run more smoothly and also to start itself much more easily. Because there are two cylinders, the engine will work quite well with no flywheel. However, a flywheel would certainly make it run a little more smoothly, and so, if you wish, make one the same as for the single, and attach it to the shaft in between the two bodies.

11 *A HORIZONTAL SINGLE-CYLINDER PISTON VALVE STEAM ENGINE*

We are now dealing with the more modern type of steam engine, if, in fact, any steam engine can be called 'modern'. This is a small piston valve engine made from stock materials; in other words, no castings are required in its construction. Although the sizes given on the drawings make for a very small model, it has a surprising

The completed engine, showing in particular the crankshaft and the cylinder cover.

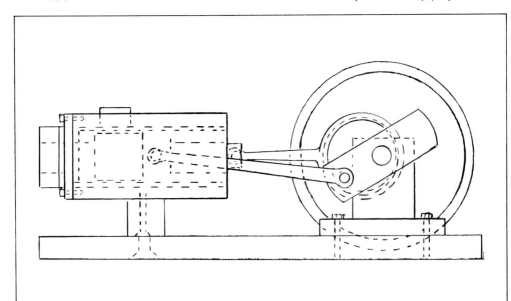

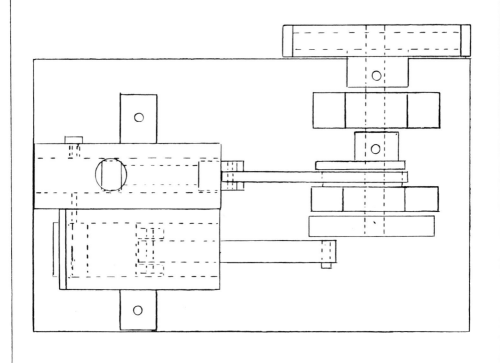

Above *The cylinder and valve chest. They are drilled separately in the four-jaw chuck and then soft soldered together at a later stage. It is best to make the cylinder cover before this soldering operation is carried out.*

Left Fig 53 *General construction details.*

amount of strength when running. Again it can be made on the smallest type of lathe.

The engine is driven by steam introduced to the valve in the valve chest. When this eccentric driven valve is open, the steam enters the cylinder and moves the piston. As the piston moves so does the valve, which itself is a small piston. The design of the valve is such that it cuts off the incoming steam and opens a small port which allows spent steam to escape as the power piston returns along the cylinder. The exhaust port is then covered by the valve and the steam port is again opened, thus re-starting the cycle.

The cylinder (Figure 54) is made from the same materials as those of the oscillating engines, and to the same dimensions. One difference here, though, is the fact that the cylinder end cover will have to be screwed into position. It is therefore made of square material and four tiny screw holes are drilled in the corners. These are transferred to the cylinder and tapped so that the cover can be bolted into position when the engine is completed. When the time comes to fix the cover in position, a small gasket should be made up to go between the cover and the cylinder to seal the joint and prevent steam escaping. If you are a do-it-yourself car enthusiast and have any liquid gasket cement material, that could always be used instead. Otherwise one will need to be cut, either from brown paper or kitchen foil; personally I prefer the latter.

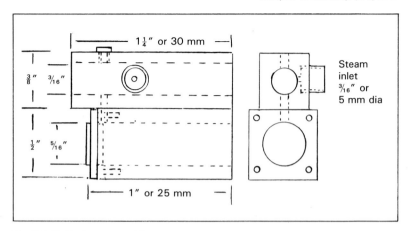

Fig 54 *Cylinder assembly.*

The valve chest is drilled first; if possible it should be reamed and then faced to length. Later it will be attached to the cylinder with soft solder, but I think it is better to sort out the fit of the valve first before joining the two parts. The shape of the valve is shown in the drawing (Figure 55). The measurements are quite important because they affect the working cycle of the engine which makes sure that things happen at the right time. The slot at the end, to take the eccentric strap, can be made with a hacksaw and very thin file, *after* drilling the cross hole for the pin.

The valve, made from brass, is a straightforward turning, drilling, sawing and filing operation.

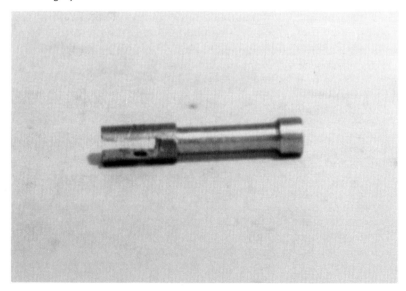

Right Fig 55 *Valve.*

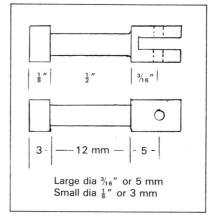

Large dia $\frac{3}{16}$" or 5 mm
Small dia $\frac{1}{8}$" or 3 mm

Below Fig 56 *Eccentric strap.*

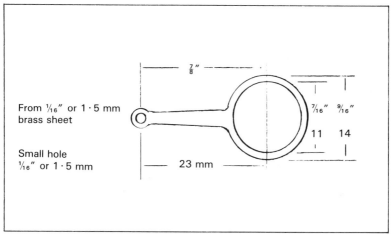

From $\frac{1}{16}$" or 1·5 mm brass sheet

Small hole $\frac{1}{16}$" or 1·5 mm

The eccentric strap (Figure 56) is a drilling and filing job. Do not leave too much material round the edges of the large hole or it will foul the base when it is assembled. The same applies to the small hole for the pin. If too much metal is left it will bind on the top of the steam chest.

The eccentric (Figure 57) is a turning job. First of all turn the lip on which the strap will run and part off the metal, slightly over the finished length. The normal way of making the off-centre hole and its boss is to mark the hole position and centre punch it, then set the work in the four-jaw chuck so that the centre pop runs true, then drill through and turn the end down to make the boss. With such a small eccentric, these operations can become quite complicated. I therefore chose to put the work in the three-jaw chuck with a suitable packing piece that will throw it off centre to exactly the correct amount, as shown in the illustration. It saves a lot of fiddling about and achieves the same end result. The final act will be to cross drill and tap one side of the boss to take a tiny grub screw.

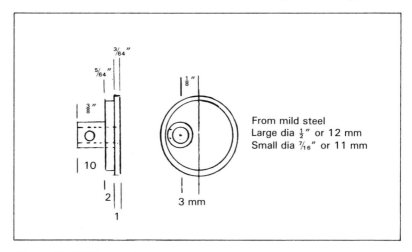

Above Fig 57 *Eccentric.*

Below *The eccentric and eccentric strap. The strap was made by drilling and filing a piece of brass, while the eccentric is turned from mild steel.*

The piston (Figure 58) is an ordinary piece of bronze, or brass if you do not have any bronze. It must be a good fit in the cylinder as no packing or piston rings will be used. The end of the piston itself is turned down and slotted, as shown in the drawing, to take the pin which will hold the piston in position, the piston rod (figure 59) is simply a drilling, sawing and filing job, as can be clearly seen in the photograph. The large end is fitted with a small bronze bearing to prevent wear. This is not the standard practice as normally the big end would be larger. However, on an engine of this size, to use a larger crank pin would make the rod look rather clumsy. In fact, sizes quoted work perfectly well.

The crank itself (Figure 60) is a piece of mild steel in which are

Above *To drill the eccentric, first turn the lip to the right diameter. Then set a piece of steel bar of the same thickness as the crank throw in the three-jaw chuck to move the component off centre while drilling operations take place.*

Below Fig 58 *Piston.*

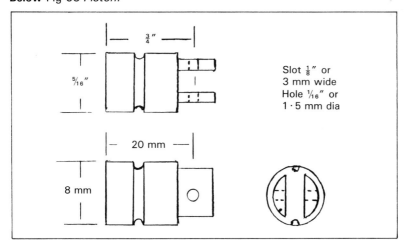

Slot $\frac{1}{8}$" or
3 mm wide
Hole $\frac{1}{16}$" or
1·5 mm dia

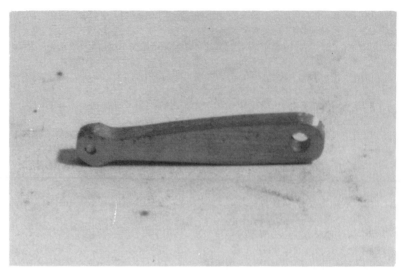

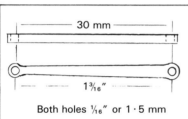

30 mm

1³⁄₁₆″

Both holes ¹⁄₁₆″ or 1·5 mm

Above *The piston rod. Both the piston and the crank shaft pins are the same size. The crank pin here has been drilled over-size and a tiny bush will be inserted before final assembly. This is to prevent excessive wear.*

Left Fig 59 *Piston rod.*

Below Fig 60 *Crank.*

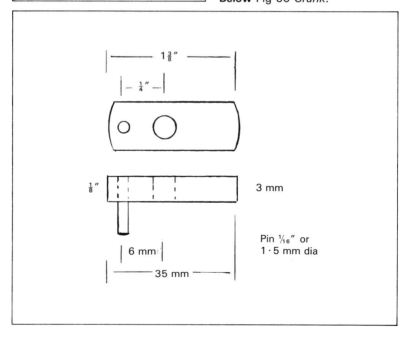

1⅜″

¼″

⅛″   3 mm

6 mm

35 mm

Pin ¹⁄₁₆″ or
1·5 mm dia

drilled two holes. The extra length at the end where there is no hole is to provide a counter balance. The crank-pin is held in position with retaining compound. The crank can either be fitted to the shaft using retaining compound or the side could be drilled and tapped to take a small grub screw.

The flywheel is similar to that on the oscillating engine and should present no problems. It will have to be cross drilled and tapped through the boss to take a grub screw.

The main bearing blocks (Figure 61) are cut from brass strip. Although two different thicknesses are shown, I made both mine from the same material. This enabled me to file one down to make a nice fit with minimum clearance between the eccentric and the crank. The bearings were made together, using the old idea of sticking them together with cyanoacrylic adhesive, drilling and cutting them, and then separating them afterwards.

The cylinder and steam chest should be soldered together with soft solder at this point. As they are of different section metal, the steam chest should be lined up so that the overlap along the length of the cylinder is equal on either side, the idea being to get both the piston and valve pins as near as possible in line, so that the ends of both components are level at the point nearest to the main bearings. This also means that the other end of the steam chest will protrude in front of the cylinder.

The soldering operation will have to be done with a blowlamp. It is possible to do it without clamping the parts together, provided

Fig 61 *Bearings.*

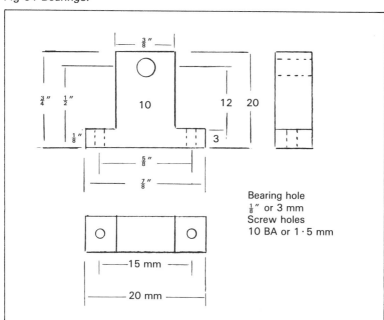

too much pressure is not applied by the blowlamp. If there is too much, then it will literally blow the parts out of line whilst heating them up. A nice gentle heat, and time taken to do the job, will make sure that there will be no problems.

It is now necessary to drill two holes through the steam chest. One, more or less central, is for the steam inlet. After centre punching, a small hole — say $\frac{1}{16}$in (1.5mm) — should be drilled right through the wall and into the bore. This should then be opened out to take a 3/16 in (5mm) thread for most but not quite all of its length. Take care here that the drill used is not too sharp. If it is, with the steam chest being of brass, there will be a tendency for the drill to snatch and probably ruin all the work already carried out. If, therefore, you quite rightly keep your drills sharp, or you are using a new one, just rub the cutting edges over with a fine piece of emery cloth and there will then be no snatching effect at all. The steam pipe is a piece of brass rod threaded to fit this hole, and through the rod should be a small hole to allow steam to pass. The same diameter as the hole you started with will do nicely.

The second hole to be drilled through the steam chest should be $\frac{1}{16}$in (1.5mm) diameter and level with the lip of the cylinder cover. This lip, by the way, should be kept as small as practical. The hole is drilled from the outside of the steam chest, through its bore, through the other side of the steam chest and then through one wall of the cylinder. It is there to provide a passage for the live steam to enter the cylinder from the steam chest and an escape for the spent steam to exhaust. However, the outside section that passes through the steam chest outer wall serves only to provide a means of drilling the connecting passage between the steam chest and cylinder, and afterwards should be tapped and fitted with a small screw to act as a plug. If this is not done, the live steam would be able to escape into the air instead of passing into the cylinder.

The cylinder is mounted on a small brass or steel bar to bring the centre of its bore in line with the centre of the bearing, as shown in the illustration. If the measurements shown have been used, the cylinder will need to be raised by $\frac{1}{4}$in (6mm), so a piece of material of this thickness will do the job. This is attached to the cylinder with tiny screws — 10BA, or 1.5mm, will be about right. The screws pass through the block of metal and into the side of the cylinder. There is not a great depth of material into which to drill so care must be taken to measure correctly. Drill the mounting block first; stick it to the cylinder block and drill through. The holes in the outside of the cylinder should be tapped; those in the mounting block opened out to clearance, and countersunk so that the screw heads will lie flush with the bottom of the block. Two outer holes can then be drilled in the mounting block. These are for screws with which the engine should be mounted to a base, for instance a piece of mild steel plate of about $\frac{1}{8}$in (3mm) thickness.

The finished engine. The steam connection is clearly visible, as is the screw sealing the hole to prevent steam escaping from the cylinder.

To assemble the engine (Figure 53) mount the cylinder assembly on the mounting block and screw it to the base. Mount the crank on its shaft and attach the piston rod, slide on the thinner bearing, attach the valve to the eccentric strap (see illustration), put it on the eccentric and fit that onto the shaft. Place the second, thicker bearing in place, slide the piston and valve into their respective bores, and see how things line up. Both the connecting rod and the eccentric strap should lie parallel with each other, and should not bind on the inner bearing block. If there is any binding, file down the bearing block, until it can be seen that it will run clear.

When all this lining up is sorted out, rotate the crank so that the piston rod pin is as far away from the cylinder as possible, then set the piston so that the edge of the thicker part just lines up with the edge of of the bore. This means that the bottom end of the piston, the piece that has been turned down, and the valve pin will be visible. Check that the shaft is at right angles to the bores and that everything is nicely lined up and then stick the bearing blocks to the base. When dry they can be used as guides for drilling the base and this should then be tapped and the bearing blocks can then be screwed into position on the base.

To achieve the correct sequence of events, remove the cylinder cover and rotate the crank until the piston can be seen at the point nearest to the end of the cylinder. This position is called top dead centre. The valve should be adjusted by turning the eccentric so that it is just allowing steam to enter through the small hole, so that as the piston starts to slide back in its bore, the valve will cut off the supply of steam. It should then go beyond the steam port just as the piston starts to move forward again. When all is correct, the cylinder cover can be replaced together with its gasket and the engine is now ready to run.

That concludes the projects contained in this little book. For most readers it will have been sufficient to provide the opportunity to potter in the workshop for a year or so! Some of you will no doubt wish to keep the projects you have just made suitably polished, as a means of demonstrating your ability. Others will be putting them to use to make even more projects. Indeed, from here on the hobby should be self-generating. I would imagine that most people will have had a year or so of enjoyment making the things described, and if my efforts have encouraged readers to think up and make their own projects, then I feel that the time I have spent writing this book will have been very worthwhile. I hope the reader has the same pleasure making the articles I have had in writing about them.

APPENDIX
ENGINEERING ADHESIVES

I have suggested the use of two types of adhesive in this book. The use of these saves a considerable amount of work and frequently makes for a more efficient finished component. These adhesives fall into two categories; anaerobic, which are referred to as retainers or retaining compounds, and cyanoacrylics, which are sometimes known as 'superglues'. The anaerobic adhesive is used for holding shafts in holes, etc, and thus can be used for securing rounded parts which would normally either need to be threaded or made as a press fit. The cyanoacrylic adhesives are generally used for securing flat surfaces, such as two metal plates, to each other.

In order to achieve success with these adhesives, the work should be free of grease; a wipe with a solvent such as carbon tetrachloride will be sufficient. If this is not available, white spirit can be used, provided the surface is dried before the adhesive is applied. To separate parts held together with cyanoacrylic adhesive, they should either be gently heated until the joint breaks, in which case avoid breathing the fumes, or tapped smartly with a copper mallet so that a sudden tearing action is produced at the joint. If one sharp tap does not do it, then heating will be necessary. In most cases where cyanoacrylic adhesive is specified, there is no need for the parts to be separated afterwards even though the use of screws or some other form of permanent fixing is advised for complete security.

Parts held together with a retaining compound can only be parted by heating. The compounds suggested have tremendous strength and for this reason are used in industry. It is indeed most unlikely that anyone working in a home workshop would have equipment available to enable these parts to be separated mechanically.

Both anaerobic and cyanoacrylic adhesives can be purchased in various strengths and viscosities. Some are not suitable for the purposes for which they have been suggested in this book. Some cyanoacrylic, for example, is sold as 'superglue'. Normal superglue will not be a suitable medium for our purpose since it is

far too thin and sets too quickly. Equally, anaerobics are sold
under names such as 'Nutlock' or 'Screwlock'. These too are not
suitable as they have insufficient strength. For this reason I
recommend the following makes and types. When purchasing, do
not just specify simply by the maker's name but ensure that the
correct type is obtained as most makers provide a variety of
strengths. There are other makes available but, as I have no
personal experience of them, I have not included them in the list;
this does not mean that they are not satisfactory, just that I
hesitate to suggest an adhesive of which I have no real
knowledge. Equally, I should add that I have no connection
whatever with the firms whose products I have suggested.

RETAINING COMPOUNDS (ANAEROBIC ADHESIVES)

Loctite 601 or 638
Zap Lock Green Formula
Permabond 168

CYANOACRYLIC ADHESIVES ('SUPERGLUES')

Loctite IS422
Flex Zap
Permabond C4

INDEX